LOONY COON

Loony Coon

Antics of a
Rollicking Raccoon

by

SAM CAMPBELL
The Philosopher of the Forest

ILLUSTRATED BY ALEXANDER KEY

THE BOBBS-MERRILL COMPANY, INC.
PUBLISHERS
INDIANAPOLIS · NEW YORK

To Giny

CONTENTS

CONTENTS—*continued*

LOONY COON

I

TROUBLE IS BORN

LOONY COON did not even wait for his baby eyes to open to get into his first batch of trouble. Giny and I were on hand to witness this primary event of his turbulent career.

It was twilight one day in early June at our island Sanctuary in Wisconsin. We cautiously approached the large dead maple tree we knew to be the home of our long-time raccoon pet Andrea. For seven years this beautiful animal had been friendly with us. Each season she used this same maple tree as her home, and each season she raised four to six youngsters here, ultimately bringing them over to our island to see and be seen.

The tree home which we call Coony Castle stands near the water's edge on the south shore of our north-woods lake. It is ideal as a raccoon residence. It is beautifully decorated with fungi and lichen, and around the exposed roots at its base is a lovely lawn of cushion moss. Six feet from the ground there is a hole a foot in diameter, the entrance to a shallow space within which are the living quarters. About Coony Castle is a vast forest, including stands of oak timber to furnish acorns for food, and many lakes whose shores are ideal hunting and fishing grounds for these active and clever animals.

11

On this eventful evening Giny and I walked quietly to the tree and pressed our ears against the bark.

"I hear voices," exclaimed Giny in an excited whisper, "baby voices!"

"There must be a nestful of them," I added, as excited as she.

Giny glanced anxiously at the hole just above our heads. "Oh, I want to see them! Would we dare to take just one little look?"

"I wonder if it would be wise?" I said, looking longingly at the hole too. "Raccoons have been known to destroy their young if they're frightened."

"But Andrea has been friendly with us so long. She wouldn't be afraid. Please . . . may we?"

My reply was to get a section of log and place it at the foot of Coony Castle. By standing on this I could look into the hole. I took a pen flashlight from my pocket and cautiously peered in. There in the shallow hollow was the neatest little huddle of raccoons I ever saw. Andrea, huge in size, was curled about her family, and it was dinnertime for all but her.

"Of all the cute sights, this one wins," I reported to the thrilled and excited Giny. "Andrea isn't the least bit frightened. In fact, she seems pleased at our call."

"Well, how many are there? What are they doing?" Giny was on her tiptoes trying to see into the hole, though this opening was only large enough to accommodate one head at a time.

"They're eating—ravenously! Andrea, what a family

of chow hounds you have! Now let's see, I can make out three . . . and there's a fourth . . . and there's a fifth. . . . Wait a minute, down under the fifth is still another! There are six! Andrea, you have the limit, and what a job you picked out for yourself."

"Let me see! Let me see!" Giny's patience was exhausted and she was tugging at my sleeve. Now it was her turn to step up on the log and look into Coony Castle. Andrea was told how lovely she was and how wonderful her family was in a way that only Giny can do.

"That one is climbing out from underneath the others,"

she informed me. "What a darling he is! I never saw a raccoon marked quite like him. There's a little white streak on his head and one ear hangs down while the other stands up. Do you hear all that racket?"

I did. There was a sudden burst of squealing and squawking from within the tree.

"Well, that one with the floppy ear is walking right on top of the others," she reported. "Why, he's stepping on their faces! He disconnects them from their dinner, and are they mad! Now he's crawling up on Andrea and has his foot in her eye."

In the excitement I had climbed up on the log beside Giny and we bumped our heads trying to look in at the same time. There was a great stir in Coony Castle, every resident yelling and clawing.

"Perhaps we're causing some of that," I suggested. "Suppose we leave them alone now. They've given us a good show."

"Oh, you wonderful little creatures!" Giny gave them one last verbal pat as we stepped down and backed away from the tree. "That one with the floppy ear and white streak is cute," she added, laughing. "Why, he just trampled all over them and his mother too."

"Well, after all, if he wants some exercise that's about the only place he can walk."

"It looked to me as if he just wanted to stir up a fuss," Giny said. "If he didn't get a reaction the first time he stepped on one of his brothers, he tried it again. Look, there he is now!"

She pointed toward the maple tree. Sure enough, there was a young raccoon balanced precariously on the edge of the hole. "Careful, Loony! You'll fall," she called. "Get back into your nest."

Loony Coon, that moment named, presented a comical appearance. His nose was pointed up in the air the way a cub does at his age. His eyes were tightly shut, as if glued together. His right ear pointed straight up, the left one drooped, and the odd white streak—a little touch of albino—stood out prominently on his head. His tail was hairless, his legs were weak and wobbly, his tummy seemed too large for the rest of him, and his nose sniffed frantically as he tried to get some hint of the great forest world about him.

"Loony Coon is the right name for him," I commented critically. "He shouldn't be moving around that way for three weeks or more. Raccoon cubs his age don't do that."

But Loony Coon had no wish to be an ordinary raccoon. He had a lifetime of mischief to live and he wanted to get going. Even as we watched he reached his front paw out into space, seeking a hold on the world beyond, and he lost his balance.

We gasped helplessly. If we rushed at him we might frighten him into a tumble, and if we didn't, likely he would fall anyway. That is just what he did. His feet slipped. For an instant there was a wild flurry of clutching and scratching, then *plunk* he landed on the soft cushion moss at the base of the tree.

Before we could make a move to help him, another

raccoon face appeared at the opening. Andrea gazed out
first at us, then at her struggling, whimpering offspring
below. Loony Coon started toward the lake in a funny
mixture of waddling, crawling and walking. Right into
the shallow waters he went, apparently not familiar
enough with the world to know land from lake. Quickly
Andrea came out of the hole, went headfirst down the
tree, then caught and dragged Loony ashore *by his head*.
It was a rescue act, but it had enough intentional punish-
ment in it to make Loony squeal.

"Oh, for our movie camera and floodlights!" I said to
Giny. "Why do such things always happen when pictures can't be made?"

My wish was echoed a dozen times within the next five
minutes. Andrea took the pesky cub by the nape of his
neck, her every move indicating a mixture of parental
love and disgust. She lifted Loony to the tree and held
him there until his tiny feet caught hold of the bark.
Then, still gripping the loose skin of his neck, she slowly
climbed back to the hole, forcing him to go through mo-
tions that would some day develop into the art of tree
climbing.

"His first lesson," I commented. "I've known raccoons
all my life, but I never saw that before."

"Look, he's up there again!" Giny cried. The woods
were darkening and our pen light was losing its power,
but we could make out Loony Coon struggling at the opening. In rapid order he went through the same routine—

balanced unsteadily, reached out with his nose, then fell *plunk* onto the moss.

This time Andrea lost her patience completely. She fairly exploded out of the tree, hurried down to the ground and snatched up her trying offspring. There was no lesson in tree climbing this time. She took him in her mouth and bit where it hurt—meaning to do it too!—then carried him squirming and squealing back home.

From the depths of the nest came more squealing.

"I believe Loony Coon is being taken to the woodshed," Giny ventured.

"He had it coming," I added unsympathetically.

The crying continued, suggesting that Loony Coon was getting spanked from one end to the other. Then it stopped abruptly and all was silent in Coony Castle.

Just before we left, Andrea looked out at us—the picture of maternal worry and discouragement. There seemed to be an apology in her expression, that a youngster of hers should put on such a display of disobedience!

"Never mind, Andrea," Giny sympathized. "Maybe he isn't bad but just ambitious. Sometimes our most headstrong children have become our best leaders. I predict Loony Coon will make his mark in this world."

"Make his mark in it?" I put in. "Why, that fellow will have it scratched from one end to the other."

II

FUNNY BUSINESS AT COONY CASTLE

THOUGH we passed by Coony Castle almost every day, it was a week before we saw any of the raccoons again. In the soft sand near the base of the tree were large and small tracks that told they were active. Perhaps there had been more *plunks* onto the moss by the high-diving Loony, followed by Andrea's rescue routine, but we did not witness them.

One evening as we were passing the maple tree I stepped close and listened. The cubs were in there all right, and the sounds I heard caused me to break out in a subdued laugh.

"What's happening?" asked Giny, coming to me. "What are they doing?"

"They're *clurping.*"

"They're what?"

"*Clurping!*"

Giny listened to the *clurping* going on within the tree and then looked at me for an explanation.

"It's an odd combination of *clucking* and *purring* they do," I said. "I know of no other animal sound like it. Remember our first raccoon pets—Rack and Ruin? They were brought to us so young their eyes were still closed. When they were hungry they made that sound."

"How in the world do they do it?" she asked. "Can you imitate it?"

I shook my head. I am not good at imitations anyway, and I believe that *clurping* is the last thing I want to do. To make the *clucking* sound, a human being would have to draw in his breath; to make the *purring* sound, he would have to exhale. To attempt doing both at once, he would probably choke and his tongue would finish in a figure-eight knot.

"I never heard of such a word as *clurping*," Giny said.

"I invented it, though I don't expect my name to go down in history for that reason. *Clurping* isn't in the dictionary, but I know what it means."

"I love *clurping*." Giny laughed, pressing her ear close to the tree. "Do you suppose I'd dare peek in and see how they do it?"

"Yes, let's have a look at them," I agreed. "It's as funny to see as to hear."

We stepped up on the log and took turns looking down at the raccoons with the aid of our pen light. Andrea was not there. No doubt she was away on a hunting trip, for she must have food and lots of it during the days when her family depends on her. Probably she had been gone for some time, for the sextuplets were famished. Coony Castle was filled with *clurping*. Giny and I laughed aloud at their actions. All six noses were pointed up in the air, all six mouths partly open as if expecting a serving of dinner any minute.

Our vaudeville show was interrupted by the arrival of Andrea. We did not hear her approaching, but suddenly she was standing right at our feet.

"Pardon us, Andrea," said Giny, backing away. "We've been watching your children put on a *clurping* chorus."

Andrea didn't need to be told. She knew these sounds only too well. Quickly she went up the tree and into the hole. The *clurping* increased greatly at first, then subsided as feeding began.

"That is the perfect way to have animals," I commented.

"Meaning?"

"Well, friendly enough so they will permit us to watch them, yet living in a wild, natural state. This is wonderful!"

As we walked away, Giny endeavored to imitate *clurping*. The effort ended in a coughing spell. Then we tried co-operation; she clucked and I purred. Together we gave a pretty good imitation of a baby raccoon.

Coony Castle and its occupants were the center of our interests as the season advanced, yet there were many other friendly creatures about the Sanctuary. Salt and Pepper, our pet porcupines, were seen once near the raccoon tree. Later Salt appeared at our cabin and stayed for several days.

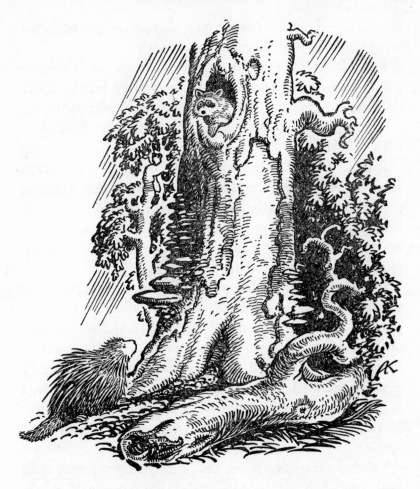

Cheer, our red-winged blackbird, was back. His mate was nesting on a little swampy island in the same low shrub they had used in previous years. He perched on our feeding station, giving his happy song, puffing up his feathers in true blackbird style, displaying proudly the bright red spots that graced his wings.

Fatty Patty Sausage, our pet woodchuck, was living in a hole under our front steps. She was still a bit thin after her long hibernation, but from the way she was eating we had no doubt that she would soon regain her blimplike figure.

Zipper, the white-tailed deer who had been our pet fawn a year ago, often came within sight and greeting distance. Occasionally she swam over to our island and came up to our cabin door to get tasty bites Giny kept ready for her. The beautiful red fox we called Zowie was seen in remote parts of the forest.

Our pet chickadees and nuthatches were back, pestering us from morning to night just as we like them to do. They perched on our shoulders and our heads and always seized on the moment when my arms were filled with wood or some other heavy load to beg for a bite of the seeds or peanut crumbs I kept in my pocket. And I, softy that I am, usually dropped whatever I was carrying and held forth an offering in my opened hand—all for the thrill of feeling their little feet on my finger tips.

Often I pretended more annoyance at these lovely little botherers than I felt. Once when Pestersome Pete, the white-breasted nuthatch, flew up giving his unmusical nasal *neeyah,* I was walking along with a large log on my shoulder. My predicament made no difference to him. So he kept pace with me, flying from tree to tree and saying in his chirping way, "How about a little handout?

Why are you wasting your time carrying trees around when you could be feeding me?"

"You feathered pest!" I blurted out at him. "Why don't you make your own living? Go on and get you some larvae, or some bugs, and don't be so lazy. You're just no good, that's all. You're the kind of a fellow who settles down to do nothing, squawking that the world owes you a living. And you think the world ought to drop it right in your lap—if you had one. You're a bum—that's what you are—just a bum."

While this futile chatter continued I was reaching into my pocket for tidbits to share with this beloved little bird. The log was out of balance and cut into my shoulder, but there wasn't a good place to put it down. The ground on which I stood was uneven. My back ached from the heavy load I was carrying. "I suppose you're satisfied at the misery you're causing me," I ranted on at Pete, who was now about arm's length from me in the crotch of a small balsam tree. "You would make a wonderful slave driver. You don't care how much trouble you cause just as long as you get what you want. Well—here!" and I thrust a handful of cracked corn and peanut bits toward him.

But Pete made no move to take the offering. He ceased his *neeyah, neeyah* and stared as though dumfounded at my words. I forgot the log and my aching shoulders and extended my hand farther toward him. Still he did not move. I began to get worried.

"Now, Pete," I said in warmer tones, "here it is. Come

and get it. That's the stuff you like so well, you know."

Pete just sat and looked at me. I moved my hand up until it was within a foot of his beak. Still no response. Always before he had been so bold in his feeding, flying to my hand without hesitation, carrying one morsel after another away to tuck under the bark of trees.

"Pete, I didn't mean it," I began apologizing. "I was only joking. You aren't a bum. You're a wonderful bird, a wonderful bird."

"What's all this jabbering about?" Giny had come up behind me.

"Why, look at Pete! I was joshing him about being a nuisance and a pest, and now it looks as though he took it seriously. Come on, Pete," I said to him pleadingly. "Do a little forgiving. I'm sorry. I apologize all over the place. I'm on my knees. I'm eating humble pie. Please just take one crumb—you're breaking my heart."

Giny coaxed and I coaxed, but the nuthatch didn't give in easily. My hand was now within three inches of his beak, and the log had seemed to increase its weight three-fold. My back ached, my shoulder ached, and my neck did too. Still Pete held out. He stretched one wing, then the other. He scratched back of his ear. At last when I had reached the limit of my endurance, and apparently he thought I had been punished enough, he calmly hopped over to my hand. There with great deliberation he se-lected the largest morsel present and carried it away, calling back "Neeyah."

"Now will you learn to be careful of your language?" Giny asked reprovingly. "You hurt his feelings."

I started away with my log, my back and shoulders now numb.

"I'll never call him a bum again," I promised, "even though he is."

III

SONYA AND A PROBLEM

THE island on which our cabin stands has only about three acres of land. It rests in the southwest portion of a moderate-sized lake. This is one of a chain of twenty-eight lakes, connected by navigable channels. Both people and animals call often at our island, and we never know who or what our guests will be.

I was sitting at my desk writing one morning when I heard the softest little tapping sound near our door. At first I thought it was a downy woodpecker working on a near-by tree. When the sound was repeated, however, it was right at the door. It is not unusual for a woodpecker to drum on our house, so as I went to the door I expected to see one of these valuable and beautiful birds fly away. But no bird was there, nor could I see anything else that might have produced such a sound.

Puzzled, I returned to my work. A moment later the tapping was repeated. No mistake about it—the sound was at the door. It came again—seven dainty but distinct taps. Giny heard it too and went to the door. She found nothing.

I stood near the closed door, determined to find out what was making this strange noise. Woodpeckers don't go around playing Halloween tricks, and I could think of no other creature that would or could be doing it. *Something* had to be there. Knocks don't go around knocking just by themselves.

I didn't have long to wait. Presently *tap, tap, tap, tap, tap, tap, tap* came in rapid succession. I jerked the door open quickly to see this whatever-it-was before it got away. There I looked into the startled face of a little girl about eight or nine years old. She was a beautiful child with very dark eyes, cameolike features against a background of long black curls. Apparently my sudden appearance had startled her, for she stood like a statue. One hand was still raised, the fingers folded to tap. She had just drawn in a deep breath that had to last a long time. Finally she managed to gasp out a little "O-h-h-h."

"Bless your heart, child, did I frighten you?" I asked, though the answer was obvious. "I'm sorry."

She kept staring at me, uncertain whether to run or not. "Are you Mr. Camp-bell?" She divided my name carefully into Camp-bell, pronouncing each syllable in a clear precise manner unusual in one of her years.

"Yes, I am Mr. Campbell," I said. "And what is your name?"

She relaxed now. Her two feet got pointed in the same direction. Her hand dropped to her side, and a lovely little smile pushed two dimples into her cheeks. "Sonya," she said clearly and then swallowed hard.

"Sonya! How nice." I took her hands in mine. "Sonya has always been a favorite name of mine. So you are the little woodpecker who has been tapping on my door. Tell me, Sonya, why did you run away?"

Her smile faded. She seemed unable to answer.

"Were you afraid?" I asked.

She nodded her head.

"Not really afraid, Mr. Campbell," said a voice. I looked up to see a well-dressed man and woman approaching the cabin. Down at the water's edge was the boat in which they had come to the island. "Sonya idolizes you. Now she's overwhelmed to be with you," the lady continued. "We're Dorothy and Richard Eck. You have already met our daughter Sonya."

Greetings were exchanged and Giny came out of the cabin to meet our surprise guests. "We ask your pardon for calling on you without invitation," said Mr. Eck, a tall man with a soft voice and quiet manners. "Sonya just had to see you. In fact we came all the way from England to call at your Sanctuary."

"From England?" I said, surprised. "I'm greatly honored."

"Well, at least you were one of the reasons that brought us here," Mrs. Eck corrected. She was a most attractive lady and dressed as if she had stepped off a fashion plate. "We've been living in England. It was there we found Sonya." She put her arm around the child and drew her into a strong hug. "She needed parents and we needed a child, so we formed a lifelong partnership."

"It looks like a partnership of love," volunteered Giny.

"It is!" agreed Mrs. Eck. "But to explain our call:

Sonya read your books—the English editions. She's
practically lived with them ever since. She loves animals.
They're her main interest, her greatest enthusiasm. She
thinks about them the way you talk of them in your books.
She wrote you once from England——"

"Wait a moment," I broke in. "Is this the Sonya who
wrote me such a nice letter a few months ago? In that
lovely handwriting?"

"Yes, it is," Mr. Eck said. "And we marveled that you
had time to answer it."

"If I had known how pretty Sonya is, I think I would
have brought the answer over in person." I laughed.

"Well, ever since receiving it Sonya was determined to
see you. We had decided to move back to America, our
native country, but seeing your Sanctuary was one of the
first things we wanted to do. Now, Sonya, you had something to ask Mr. Campbell. What was it?"

Sonya had recovered entirely from her shock now. She
looked up at Giny and me, smiled in between two dimples
and said, "Is Inky the porcupine real?"

"Yes, he's a very real porcupine."

"Are Salt and Pepper the porcupines real too?"

"Yes, they're very real too."

"And Sausage the woodchuck, Rack and Ruin the raccoons, Bobette the deer . . ." and she went on to name a
long list of animals we have known at the Sanctuary. She
was assured they were all real animals and that our friendships with them were real too.

As we were talking I heard a nuthatch's call overhead.

"Sonya," I said, "right this minute you're going to meet Pestersome Pete."

"Oo-oo! Now who is this Pestersome Pete?" she said, eyes wide with interest.

"Pestersome Pete is our pet nuthatch," I replied. "Here, take these peanut crumbs and hold them out in your hand. I'm sure he'll come to you."

Pete didn't hesitate. With a little call of *neeyah*—probably the equivalent of "whoopee"—he flew right up and perched on her finger tips.

Sonya gave a gasp of delight. She was fascinated with Pete, and he with her. Instead of snatching a morsel and flying away, he remained on her hand, looking up into

her face as much as to say, "Where have you been all my life?"

Sonya said nothing, though her dark sparkling eyes told something of the joy she was experiencing.

I chanced to glance at Mrs. Eck's face. Her expression was puzzling. Far from showing the happiness I expected, her eyes were shadowed with something closely akin to fear. Her hands closed tightly and she kept her gaze fixed on Sonya.

When Pete at last flew away from Sonya's hand, she whirled about and pressed into her mother's arms. "Mother, Mother, did you see Pete?" she cried. "Did you see him, right on my hand?"

"Yes, yes, I saw him, dear," said her mother, a smile breaking through. "You're very happy now, aren't you?"

There was no question about that. "He'll come back, Sonya," I said, giving her more peanut crumbs. "Our chickadees too will come soon, and they'll light right on your hand."

"We must not take too much of your time," said Mr. Eck. "It's wonderful to be here and Sonya won't forget it. While she's feeding the birds, could Mrs. Eck talk with you for just about five minutes?"

"Of course," I said.

Pestersome Pete was back on Sonya's willing hand and Giny was calling up the chickadees as Mrs. Eck and I walked a few steps away.

"I'm afraid you're going to think me very silly, Mr. Campbell," she began speaking hesitantly as if uncertain how to present her subject. "I have a problem, a serious one for me. Mr. Eck feels sure you can help me, and I'll be so grateful if you can."

"I'll be happy if I can be of any service to you," I said. Then looking back to the group feeding birds where Sonya was squealing with delight, I added, "Just see the joy that sweet child is getting out of feeding those birds."

"That's the point," said Mrs. Eck, facing toward them. "It's that joy I want to preserve, and my problem is how to do it."

"I don't quite understand."

"Mr. Campbell, love for animals is the dominant thing in Sonya's life. She reads about animals, talks about them, dreams about them, thinks about them almost all the time."

"A wholesome thing," I commented. "It will be a source of pleasure all through her life, something that will never fail."

Mrs. Eck was silent for a moment, evidently uncertain how to go on. "Mr. Campbell," she said seriously, "she loves every living thing. It's her nature to do so. The question is, can a person who doesn't like animals *learn* to love them?"

"Why do you ask?"

"Because . . . well, frankly . . . I can't stand animals! Maybe I'm afraid of them, maybe I hate them, I don't know. It isn't just certain kinds of animals, I don't want any of them near me. Even that bird! I know he's cute and beautiful and all that, but it made me cringe to be so near him. Shivers like young earthquakes ran all over me."

I looked at her incredulously. "Is it a so-called allergy?" I asked.

"No. At least it doesn't make me ill—only creepy. I've talked to some of my friends who feel that way about snakes. But I'm like that about *any* animal. It wasn't such a problem before I found Sonya. I was leading a busy life, and didn't have animals around me. But now, don't you see, I must overcome this aversion some way, for Sonya has to have animals and I have to have Sonya. I can't let this be a barrier between us; I must learn to see them as she does."

"Sonya does have pets?" I asked.

"Mr. Campbell, we now live in a suburb of Chicago. Sonya has brought home frogs, toads, turtles, snakes, worms, puppies, kittens—until I've gone nearly crazy. Animals seem to know my feelings, and they do awful things to me. Sonya was showing me her favorite frog. It took one look at me, and then jumped on my shoulder and went down my back inside my dress. I nearly passed out. Sonya thought I was laughing, but I was hysterical. Her dogs bite me, her cats scratch me. She once had an owl that would just sit and hoot at me. They all know I don't like them. Now, Mr. Campbell, you love animals the way Sonya does. How am I going to learn? What is the secret?"

I was searching for something to say that would be helpful. Many times I have met people who have no natural love for animals. As a rule they have no wish to change their thinking. In fact, this was the first time I had known anyone who actually wanted to conquer the condition.

"I guess I got a wrong start with animals," Mrs. Eck was saying. "At our home when I was a child, we had no pets. And most of the books I read about wild animals taught how savage they were. Even now I imagine that bears just go around hugging people, wildcats jump on you out of trees, snakes sneak up on you, eagles carry children away, skunks spray you, rabbits jump at you, wolves bark at you——"

"Wolves don't bark, they howl," I broke in, laughing. "Snakes don't sneak, eagles don't snatch children. In fact, rarely is any animal an enemy of a human being—almost never in this part of the world. Animals quickly sense it if anyone is afraid of them, because they feel it means hostility. These notions you have are fairy tales. Like ghosts and goblins, they're not true. Your whole problem is the way you're thinking about animals. Surely we ought to be able to correct and readjust thoughts that aren't true. I suggest you study animals, get facts about them, learn how intelligent they are, get nearer to them and rid yourself of the errors you hold about them. You have a sense of humor about the situation. That will help tremendously."

"Perhaps you're right," she said doubtfully. "I'll try. We've rented a summer home near here for the season. Would you mind if we came over to your Sanctuary to see some of your pet animals once in a while? If you enjoy them the way your books indicate, surely I can learn from watching you. I don't want to be a martyr and suffer while Sonya enjoys her nature pals. I want to be really happy with them." Her next words were emphasized by a stamp of her foot. "I vow I'm going to live this season so close to nature I can hear her snore." Mrs. Eck's eyes narrowed in determined resolve. "I don't want to walk just hand in hand with nature, I want to get my arms about her. I'm going to stay out in the forest so much I'll look like one of the trees. And if I can stand it I want to get so friendly with animals they will pat me on the back and call me by my first name. Now please be frank with me. Would it bother you terribly if we came here occasionally—not only for Sonya's sake, but for mine?"

I assured her they would be most welcome, requested that their coming be by appointment so as not to interrupt picture taking. I suggested books she might read that would give correct information about animals.

Then we went back to the group who were still having fun with the birds. Giny was feeding chickadees out of both hands, Mr. Eck was tossing peanuts to our pet blue jay and watching him catch them in mid-air. Sonya was happily bewildered trying to see all that was going on.

Pestersome Pete was in the height of his glory. He rushed back and forth until his wing feathers were frazzled, carrying peanut crumbs from Sonya's ever-ready hand and storing them under the bark of near-by trees. Each time he returned, Sonya showered him with flattery.

"Oh, Pete, you're beautiful, you're lovely, you're won-derful!" she exclaimed over and over again. Pete just soaked it up.

As I approached he looked over at me as much as to say, "Listen, Old Top, and you'll learn how you ought to talk to a bird like me."

"May I feed him?" asked Mrs. Eck from between clinched teeth.

"Please do, Mother," said Sonya. "It's so much fun."

Mrs. Eck took some peanut crumbs from Sonya. When she held them out, her hand trembled. She drew her head back and closed her eyes as if she expected an explosion. Pete came sailing in and lighted on her hand. Suddenly he discovered this wasn't Sonya. Then he did something I have seldom seen a nuthatch do. He deliberately hauled off and gave Mrs. Eck's hand a sharp and painful peck.

"Ee-e-e-e-ek!" screamed Mrs. Eck, jerking her hand away.

"Neeyah!" yelled Pestersome Pete, sailing away like a jet plane.

Chickadees were flying in various directions and Blooey the blue jay headed for the clouds!

That was the end of bird feeding for the day. Even the pleading calls of Giny and Sonya could not get them to return.

"You see what I mean?" said Mrs. Eck to me, as the commotion subsided.

IV

WINGED DANGER FOR LOONY COON

OUR next adventure with Loony Coon was a bit frightening. It came on one of those silent mystery-soaked nights which nature compounds occasionally. Moonbeams make the world strange, and the forest bears a touch of fantasy.

Giny and I were out in our canoe, the only mode of travel in harmony with the mood of the moment. Resting our paddles, we floated motionlessly on the mirrored waters between our island and the shore where Coony Castle stands. Despite the bright moonlight a few stars peered through to add the loveliness of their twinkling eyes to the evening, and intermittently meteors traced their paths through the heavens with fading fingers of light.

Then there was a presence in the air close over our heads. We heard the soft, breathy sound of wings as some creature of great size swept by. The fleeting form of a large bird was etched against the sky.

"What was *that?*" Giny asked in a whisper.

"I believe it was an owl," I replied.

"As large as that?"

"Yes. The great horned owl has a wingspread up to five feet. That may have been one."

My thought was confirmed a few minutes later when from out the black shadows of the mainland came a pierc-

ing, catlike cry—the hunting call of the great horned owl.

"Oh, what an eerie call!" Giny exclaimed. "It gives me goose pimples."

"That seems the purpose of it," I said. "It spreads fear among the small animals of the forest. When they're bewildered with fear they're easy victims for the owl."

"He's a great hunter, isn't he?"

"The greatest among predatory birds. He's called by nature students the 'Tiger of the Air.' As a fighter and predator he's supreme."

"Do men like him?" Giny asked.

"Well, from the human view he's both good and bad. Much of his food consists of mice, rats and other small creatures who increase to harmful numbers unless controlled. The trouble is, he develops fancy and specialized tastes. Occasionally a great horned owl decides he's going to live on domestic fowl—chickens, ducks and guinea hens. That puts him in bad with the farmer. Other kinds of owls are benefactors of mankind, but this fellow gets wrong ideas about his food, so he's an outlaw as far as men are concerned."

We had been speaking in low voices. In the distance we could trace the movements of the owl by his repeated call. He was quiet for a few minutes, and then the call came from a point on the dark shore in the vicinity of Coony Castle.

"Would he harm Loony Coon?" Giny asked anxiously.

"Indeed he would, if he got the chance."

"But Andrea could protect her young, couldn't she?"

"I believe so—yet that owl is a fierce fighter."

The cry of the owl came again, and our concern mounted. Sound travels far on a silent night. We heard something like the breaking of twigs. I began paddling, directing the canoe toward Coony Castle.

"Let's hurry," Giny urged, stroking strongly at bow paddle. "I've the feeling we're needed there."

We ran the canoe aground at the nearest point convenient to the raccoon tree. As we did the big owl took to wing from the top of a near-by hemlock. Doubtless he had discovered the home of the raccoons. Perhaps a tragedy had already occurred. I knew it was unlikely that he would raid the nest itself, inside the tree, but the possibility that Loony Coon had been caught outside concerned me. I tried to catch the owl in the ray of my flashlight to see whether he had game in his talons, but he was too fast and vanished into the darkness.

"Loony Coon, Loony Coon!" moaned Giny as she hastened over to the tree, climbed on the log and looked in. "Andrea isn't here," she reported.

"No doubt hunting," I replied. "How many are there?"

"They're so tangled I can hardly tell," she returned. "I see one, two, three, four, five—five noses. But, Sam, none of these little ones has a floppy left ear or white on his head. Loony Coon is gone! Oh, just let me get my hands on that owl!"

She stepped down and looked into the trees as if she meant to take off after him at once.

I flashed my light about the ground, looking for evidence of a struggle. The usual raccoon tracks were at the base of the tree, nothing more. Then we heard a slight rustling a few feet away in a pile of brush. Something was moving about. Quickly we went to the spot and looked in among the branches.

"It's he!" exclaimed Giny delightedly. "It's Loony

Coon. Come out here, you little scamp. Don't you know there's a big owl just looking for the likes of you? Oh, why do you leave your nest when your mother isn't around?"

Loony Coon, now in the full ray of our flashlight, had grown since we last saw him. His eyes were open. He was still fat, awkward and comical-looking, and very much a baby. Giny was reaching for him when I restrained her for a moment to look at something I had discovered. Over an area of four or five feet the leaves had been blown back and there were plain marks where wing tips had struck the sand. Twigs were broken in the brush pile at this point and there were several deep gashes cut in heavy limbs.

"What does it mean?" Giny asked.

"The owl undoubtedly made a try for him," I explained, interpreting the marks. "The bird came down with much force, breaking the twigs and beating the ground with his wings. He bit into these branches with his beak. Only the brush saved Loony Coon, and perhaps the owl would have got him anyway if we hadn't arrived when we did."

"Loony Coon!" Giny reached into the brush and brought him out by the loose skin on his neck. "What can I do to make you realize the danger you've been in?" She snuggled him in her arms. "Listen to that, Loony," she added, shaking him a little. The owl had just called back in the black forest. "Don't you understand that bird is inviting you to dinner? Only you'd be the dinner. You must stay in your nest when your mother isn't around. If you don't . . ." She didn't finish the sentence. Loony Coon had begun *clurping*. Giny touched the end of his nose with her finger and he immediately took it in his mouth and tried nursing on it.

She carried him over and placed him in his nest. "Let's stay right here and guard him from that owl," she suggested.

"It would be a twenty-four hour job each day."

"Are owls about in the daytime too? I always heard they could see only at night."

"Owls see well at night but they see and hunt in daylight too," I replied. "I'm afraid Loony Coon must meet his own problem."

Giny was silent for a moment, looking thoughtfully in the direction from which we heard the owl. "Sam," she said, "I've never wanted to destroy anything. But I wonder if we shouldn't destroy that owl. It would be awful if he caught Loony Coon."

"That thought came to me too," I answered, "but we can't do it. This is a game sanctuary and all living things are protected here. Anyway, that owl is merely carrying on his part in the forest scheme. It's just unfortunate that his hunting habits threaten animals in which we have special interest. Listen—there's his other call."

Out of the night came the eerie hollow tones generally referred to as *hoots*. They echoed through the dark chambers of the woods and then died away, leaving the silence deeper than ever.

"I wouldn't want a forest without that voice," I said. "Something of wilderness would be gone. Nature must have predators as well as nonpredators, you know."

"Yes, I know." Giny was unconvinced. "But do we have to stand by and see animals that are our personal friends caught and destroyed? Our pets bring joy to so many people. They're more important than just a meal for some old owl."

"Yes, I'm sure you're right," I agreed. "We would be justified in protecting them in every way we can. But we can't destroy that owl. Maybe we can discourage him so he'll hunt elsewhere, but . . ."

We were interrupted by the return of Andrea. She came right up to us and accepted some peanuts from our hands. While she was eating the owl called again. Instantly Andrea stopped eating, rose on her hind feet and peered into the night. Then she went hastily into Coony Castle. As she entered, a chorus of *clurping* greeted her, silenced a moment later when dinner began. We did not tell Andrea we had found Loony Coon outside the nest and thus likely saved him from another trip to the woodshed.

"She knows more about that owl than we do," I commented to reassure Giny as well as myself. "I feel certain she'll be on her guard."

We paddled back to our island in silence. The night sparkled with muted glory. Deep in the black woods the owl called rhythmically, monotonously, ominously.

V

SONYA MEETS GINY BUBO

OUR next brush with the great horned owl came at dusk one day soon after Loony Coon's narrow escape.

Nightly he was in evidence. We named him Giny Bubo. His scientific name is *Bubo virginianus,* and I twisted that around and rearranged it to suit the purpose. We didn't know whether the bird was male or female as owl ladies and gentlemen dress alike. However, by using the name Giny Bubo part of the time and the pronoun *he* at others, we were sure to be right occasionally.

Giny Campbell accepted the name for the owl under protest. "With all the nice animals we have around, why would you have to call that owl Giny?" she complained. "I'm having such a hard time to like him—and now you give him my name!"

But the name stuck.

Vainly we wished he would go elsewhere, but apparently he decided he had struck a most happy hunting ground. No doubt his sharp eyes had noted the large number of animals about our home, and he planned to settle down to a life of luxury and abundance.

One long June evening we arranged for Sonya to visit Coony Castle. That scene should have been televised. It would be difficult to find more joy and happiness in one earthly spot than we saw there. The Eck family came by boat, and in our canoe we led them to the shore where the hollow maple stub was standing. Giny made sure Andrea was at home and in proper mood to receive company. Then she gave Sonya a flashlight and asked her to peek into the tree. The child was so excited she could not do it at first. She was trembling from head to foot. When at last she looked down on the raccoon family, we thought she was going to climb right through the hole.

"Oh, Mother, Father, was there ever anything so wonderful?" she squealed with delight. "Just look at these darling creatures!" And then she reached a pitch of enthusiasm where no words would suffice and she kept exclaiming, "Oh! Oh! Oh!"

"Tell me, Sonya," said Giny, "is there one little cub with a floppy ear and a white streak on his head?"

"Yes, there is. I've been watching him. He's cute."

"Well, that's Loony Coon. He's the one we think is such a problem child."

"What's the mother's name?" she asked.

"Andrea."

"Andrea! She's a good and patient mother." The happy child giggled. "Why, Loony Coon is biting her in the face. Now he's walking right over the others, stepping on them. He's biting each one. He's awful! Oh, Andrea looks so proud of her family!" Sonya brought her head out of the tree and looked at us. "I'm being very selfish," she said apologetically. "I'm not giving anyone else a chance to see, am I? Come, Father, you must look."

Mr. Eck took his turn and in a somewhat restrained way reported that Loony Coon was still disturbing the household and that Andrea seemed especially fond of her naughty cub. She was carefully caressing and washing Loony.

Next Mrs. Eck went to the tree. She hesitated, suggesting, "Maybe we hadn't better disturb them any more."

"Oh, I'm sure they don't mind," Giny said. "Andrea always likes people."

"All people?" Mrs. Eck asked.

"Yes, all people."

"Well, here goes."

Mrs. Eck bravely stepped up on the log, drew in one deep breath as if she thought it her last one and literally thrust her head into the tree opening. Whether she did it too quickly or what I do not know, but something suddenly changed the mood in Coony Castle. There was a series of angry growls from the tree. With a long high-pitched "Ee-e-e-ek" Mrs. Eck jerked her head out, leaped from the log and ran behind another tree.

Andrea looked out of the hole with an expression of belligerence I had never seen on her face before. Mr. Eck consoled his wife while Sonya apologized to Andrea. "Did Mother frighten you, Andrea?" she said solicitously as she went to the tree.

"Did I frighten *her?*" said Mrs. Eck, recovering her breath. "What did she do to me?" Then she added in a low voice, "And I read about raccoons for hours before I came here."

Just before sunset Mr. and Mrs. Eck went fishing and Giny and I took Sonya for the first canoe ride of her life. It was a lovely evening and the child was thrilled. Night-hawks were circling overhead.

"Do you hear that peculiar sound they make as they dive?" Giny asked.

Sonya had been listening to it.

"Well, that's the air rushing through their wings."

We were to learn that Sonya need not be told the same fact twice. She had a remarkable memory and a capacity for nature knowledge.

"And what's that sound?" she asked, pointing in the direction from which a voice came.

I listened and made out the distant cry of the owl Giny Bubo. He wasn't using the hunting cry now, it was his hoot call repeated again and again. Giny told Sonya of our experience with the owl and how he had attacked Loony Coon.

"But I hear two of them now," Sonya said. "There's another voice away far off."

We listened carefully and sure enough, there was a second owl calling.

"I'm glad you discovered them, Sonya," I said. "Here's something I've been wanting Giny to hear, and you'll want to notice it too. You're listening to two different species of owl."

"Are we?" Sonya asked. "They sound just the same to me."

"And to me too, Sonya," said Giny.

"There's a difference," I insisted. "Listen carefully. The one to the left is Giny Bubo. Notice he goes *hoo, hoo-hoo, hoo, hoo*—the second and third *hoo-hoos* are close together. He changes the number of *hoots,* sometimes giving three of them, sometimes five, sometimes six."

The two listened closely and verified this rhythm.

"Now listen to the other voice. That's the barred owl. He's a nicer fellow around farms, not apt to attack poultry. He gives his hoots in two groups of four, eight calls in all. For this reason he's sometimes called the 'eight-hooter.' "

"Yes," exclaimed Sonya, "I counted them! There were eight *hoos.* And I noticed something else. The one to the right, the——"

"Barred owl."

"Yes, the barred owl drops his voice on the last hoot."

"That's right, Sonya," I agreed. "You're a good observer. His last hoot is *hoo-aah,* with a downward inflection. That's an easy way to distinguish the two. You'll always know the calls of the great horned owl and the barred owl now."

"Isn't it fun to learn things about nature, Sonya?" Giny commented.

But Sonya did not hear her. Her attention was focused on an object far ahead of the canoe.

"That's a family of wild ducks, Sonya," I said, following her gaze, "a mother and six or seven young. What graceful swimmers they are!"

The ducks were working their way into the west bay of our lake. This bay has a swampy area with many

stumps sticking out of the water and tangled marginal brush. I presumed the ducks were going back into this area for shelter during the night, and very possibly they had nested there.

A lovely sunset was developing in the west. For a few minutes our attention was drawn to that. A great blue heron leisurely flapped his way through the sky silhouetted against pink clouds. High above the level of the heron a bald eagle was circling in effortless flight.

"An eagle!" exclaimed Sonya, much excited. "Oh, I've always wanted to see an eagle."

"Well, there he is," I said. "Can you see the white at his head and tail, though his underside is dark? That's how you identify him. There's another bird called the osprey which flies much the same way. But he's all white underneath so you can easily distinguish him."

"And what was that?" Giny asked. From the depths of the bay came a cry that had a quality of fear in it. It was the voice of a duck but one in distress. Our little family of ducks had disappeared into the shore-line shadows and the cry came from the direction they had taken.

"Something may have caught one of those ducks," I suggested.

"Oh, no," Sonya objected. "What would do that?"

"Well, a turtle, or a muskellunge."

"A what?"

"A muskellunge—a large savage type of fish we have in the north."

But at that moment another voice spoke up that told me the story. It was the hunting cry of Giny Bubo with which we were already too familiar.

"It's that owl!" I stated. "He's after those ducks. His call is from the very place they went."

"Oh, why doesn't he go some place, *any* place," Giny moaned. "Couldn't you learn to talk owl to him, Sam, and tell him to go away—to Africa or to the moon?"

"*Hoo, hoo-hoo, hoo, hoo*—me?" I asked, then added quickly, "I see him. Look in that tall dead tree silhouetted against that low cloud. He's in the very top of it."

Sonya and Giny had to search for a moment but they found him.

His call came regularly now and so did the distress cry of the ducks. We were paddling as rapidly as we could and still avoid the many roots and stubs of trees. As we got deep into the bay, the look of things was all too plain to us.

"The ducks have taken shelter under that overhanging brush at the shore line, Sonya," I explained. "It isn't much protection, but it has saved them so far. No doubt Giny Bubo is just figuring out a way to attack them."

We were close enough now to see the family of ducks, the little ones huddled about the mother. If the young did not realize their danger, the old mother was fully aware of it. She knew the few slender bushes standing between them and that master hunter offered little protection. In desperation she kept repeating that heart-rending cry. If she remained where she was, the owl would attack sooner or later; if she tried to swim away and thus enter open water, she was at his mercy.

So intent were the birds on their problem that neither owl nor ducks noticed us until we were quite close. When they finally discovered us there was confusion among the ducks and much resentment by Giny Bubo. His cry became almost a shriek as he screamed his rage at us.

I had to ask Sonya to sit down in the canoe. She was

so excited and so in sympathy with the beleaguered ducks that she seemed ready to jump overboard and swim to their rescue.

The ducks had a difficult decision to make. Coming toward them was man, the kind of creature that destroys countless thousands of their kind every year with his thundering guns. High above in the trees was their age-old enemy the owl.

"Doesn't she know we're here to help her?" Sonya asked.

"Yes, I think she does," I replied. "See, she's getting her young ones close about her."

"Look, bless her heart, she's coming right to us!" Giny exclaimed. From her seat in the bow of the canoe she could see better than Sonya or I.

Logs now blocked our path so that we could get no nearer the ducks, but under the leadership of the mother they were sailing out to meet us.

Giny Bubo looked down and yelled his frustration. Here was a choice duck dinner, well within reach. Those ducks were in the open water, but they were too close to the canoe for him to attack. Fear of us held him back. He stretched his great wings. He pranced back and forth on the branch where he had perched. He raised his feathers until he looked twice normal size. In fact, so threatening was his attitude that I wondered if I would have to fight him off with my canoe paddle—something I did not want to do, for it is hazardous to move about that way in a canoe.

Giny Bubo did not attack. He contented himself with hurling uncomplimentary epithets at the ducks, at us, and probably at all of our kind.

"Look, look!" exclaimed Sonya, delighted at the turn of events. "Why, those ducks are so close I could almost touch them."

The mallard and her young had come within a paddle's length of the canoe. She looked at us as much as to say, "You wouldn't take advantage of us, would you—harm us when we're trying to get away from that old so-and-so up there?"

"You're safe, you fine old mother," Giny said in low voice. "Nothing's going to hurt you or your babies if you stay close to us."

Stay close she did! I began sculling the canoe away from the shore. Our little feathered flotilla kept pace with us, making every turn we did.

"This is the first time I ever convoyed a family of ducks through the battle zone," I commented cheerily, feeling that we had triumphed.

"Isn't it wonderful?" Sonya cried.

We paddled on into the open lake, the ducks staying right beside the canoe. The sunset had faded and the afterglow hung in the northwest. We talked to the ducks and they quacked and babbled to us. Neither knew just what the others were saying, but likely their quacking had much to do with Giny Bubo, his ancestors and his ancestors' ancestors.

"Do you suppose they can fly?" Sonya asked.

The ducks answered the question. Now with a broad lake before them, they spurted ahead led by the mother and gracefully took to the air. Choosing a course directly away from the scene of their near tragedy, they disappeared into the darkened east.

"Well, Bubo," said Giny, looking back toward the west, "we whipped you that time."

"Hoo, hoo-hoo, hoo, hoo?" came Bubo's voice from far back in the forest.

VI

GRANDMAW HONKER ET AL.

THE morning mail brought a welcome letter. It was post-marked from a small town back in the woods about a hundred miles north of us. The handwriting was large and rough and our names were misspelled. However, we knew the sender and opened the letter eagerly. Giny read it aloud.

Dear Folks:

You better go 'head and get up here fast. Grandmaw Honker is come back and is funnier and bossier than ever. You got to see her play with my two otters Mike and Ike. They are both shees but I call them that anyway. Hurry up.

Yours,
WARDEN OLIE

"Warden Olie—bless his heart!" Giny exclaimed. "How good to hear from him!"

"And Grandmaw Honker is back," I added. "Do you remember her?"

"Do I? She's the largest Canadian goose I ever saw."

"And the cutest."

"And the funniest and sauciest." Giny's recollection

came with enthusiasm. "Sam, we *must* drive up there."

Just to see our friend Warden Olie was sufficient inducement to make the drive. He was a man of unusual character, strong and as ruggedly honest as the pine trees among which he had lived all his life. His love of nature and particularly animals had led him to settle on the shore of a small wilderness lake. He owned a beautiful section of forest land, and he stubbornly refused to sell any portion of it or permit the timber to be cut. Here he had built six log cabins, backwoods style, and the renting of these to vacationers was his only source of income.

Warden Olie had a long name of Scandinavian vintage, but it was too difficult for people to pronounce, so he took the short one by which everyone in the region knew him. He wasn't a game warden, never had been, but his zeal in protecting forest animals had earned him the honorary title. He was a keen and careful observer of animal ways, and naturalists of high scholastic standing respected his conclusions.

His age he never told, but we gathered that he had worked in logging camps more than sixty years ago. Yet his posture was upright, his hair and dense crop of whiskers were barely tinted with gray, his stride in the woods was a challenge to the hardiest man. Warden Olie was intensely religious, and while he seldom talked about it, his philosophy was reflected in his actions. He lived alone and liked it.

"Alone?" he said once when someone tried to sympathize with him. "Why, I go-'head and have more friends

than you do in the city. I got birds that call on me ever'
mornin' and deer that go-'head and follow me like dogs,
and a fox that comes to my door. And my friends never
talk about me behind my back nuther. Bet yourn do!"

Giny and I laughed as we recalled how he used the
phrase *go-'head* apparently for emphasis, but often in the
oddest places. Though Warden Olie had lived long among
rough men, he had never been known to swear. Sometimes when he wanted to describe something very special,
he would lengthen his pet phrase to *go-'head-in-there.*

"Remember when he said that Grandmaw Honker was
the best go-'head-in-there goose in the north country?" I
asked, laughing.

"Yes, and I remember he thought a certain sunset was
go-'head-in-there beautiful." Then Giny's eyes lighted
with anticipation. "Do you know what we ought to do?"

"What?"

"Take the Ecks with us. They'd love Warden Olie and
he'd love them. Maybe Grandmaw Honker would help
Dorothy understand animals."

"A grand idea. Let's ask them, and pray that Grandmaw is in a good mood when we go."

The Ecks were all for it. We called at their cabin the
morning we were on our way to Warden Olie's. Briefly
we told them about the old woodsman and his letter.
Would they like to go?

Would they? The very cabin vibrated with their enthusiasm. In fifteen minutes by the clock they were ready
and we headed down the highway.

"Oh, you're wonderful to take us along!" Dorothy exclaimed.

"Yes, wonderful," Dick said in his soft voice.

"Wonderful," echoed Sonya, charged with excitement.

Dorothy, Dick and Sonya we called them now—and they called us Giny and Sam. Last names are a nuisance among friends.

We drove over a hundred miles of lovely north-country roads, and then turned off the main highway and down the narrow winding lane that led to Warden Olie's homestead.

Olie was there to greet us. He emerged from the back door of his cabin and walked toward our car with a stride that covered the distance quickly. He looked like a typical lumberjack. Though the day was hot, he wore a wool shirt. The sleeves were rolled up halfway to his elbow. His trousers were supported by bright-red suspenders, and the cuffs were rolled well above the ankles, revealing his moccasin-type boots. His hair and whiskers were about as tangled as a hazel-brush thicket with no two hairs pointing exactly the same way.

The Ecks had been warned about his candor. He had a well-deserved reputation of saying just what came to his mind regardless of how it sounded to others. As soon as one understood him, his manners were not offensive, but the first experience was often quite a shock. I recalled what he said when I was introduced to him months before. "Howdy," he blurted. "Yer jist a sawed-off shrimp, ain't ye? I don't see how you go-'head and get about the woods with them short legs of yourn. Ye must go-'head and spend half yor time astraddle a log."

To little Sonya he gave a smile that spread his whiskers all about the compass. "Pleased to meetcha, Sonya," he said. " 'Bout all I miss round here is a nice young-'un like you."

"I'm glad to meet you too, Warden Olie," she replied.

Dorothy Eck didn't fare so well. "Why all the fine toggery?" he asked, a twinkle in his eyes. "Did ye think you was a-goin' some place? Them duds fit here about like an orange tree would."

Dick Eck got a blunt reception. "Eck, eh?" said Warden Olie as he shook hands. "Ain't much of a name but it's easy to say, and I guess you know what it means."

"Yes, I answer to it, Warden Olie," said Dick. "We're grateful for the privilege of coming to your place and hope we're not intruding."

"Nope, nope—glad you came. Hope you go-'head and come often." Warden Olie smoothed his rebellious whiskers and pushed his hair back but whiskers and hair all resumed their former disheveled position immediately.

"How do you make a livin', Eck?" he asked bluntly.

"I'm an engineer," Dick said smiling.

"Ye mean on a railroad?" Warden Olie motioned as if pulling on a whistle cord.

"No, I build things."

"Oh, I get it. Well, good fer you. That's nice work. Ye know I'm sorta that way myself. I built ever' one of these go-'head-in-there cabins, and not one of 'em leaks."

"Warden Olie," Sonya broke in, "where is Grandmaw Honker?"

Warden Olie's expression changed to a smile that even his whiskers could not hide. "So you been a-hearin' 'bout Grandmaw, have ye?" he said, turning to walk toward his lake. "S'pose Sam and Giny have been tellin' you. Come along, we'll find Grandmaw."

The cabins Warden Olie had built were of heavy logs and presented a most sturdy appearance but with no architectural niceties and refinements. Those he rented out were located down the lake shore, reached by a winding path that circled among stumps and trees and over bumpy roots and stones.

The cabin in which he lived was larger than the others. The interior was one large room, a combination of library, laboratory, museum and living quarters. Precious little of it was devoted to living quarters. In one corner was a cot on which he slept, a low wood stove for heating and cooking and a few dishes and supplies. The rest of the room was filled with cabinets, crowded bookshelves, relics of early logging days, files, and a desk on which rested a microscope.

Olie showed us about his cabin with considerable pride. Obviously he loved his home. From the shelves he took volume after volume inscribed to him by various authors. He had us sign his guest book. "Ye'll go-'head and be in good company there," he assured us, pointing out names of prominent people from every walk of life who had visited his place.

"How clean his cabin is!" Dorothy whispered to me on the side. "There isn't a speck of dirt anywhere."

"Hev ye seen my goes-in-it and goes-out-it?" Olie asked suddenly.

"Your what?" I asked.

"My goes-in-it and goes-out-it?" Olie repeated. "Here 'tis, back o' th' stove." He led us to where we could see a hole about a foot square cut in his floor.

"That's it," he said with an air of satisfaction. "My animals goes-in-it and then they goes-out-it. Saves me openin' th' door a hundred times a day."

"Now who in the world uses that entrance?" Dorothy asked.

"Oh, my fox, my otters, my cat, my rabbit. My bear used to come in, but he got too big. Gone wild now, like he ought to. I never know who'll go-'head and call on me."

Dorothy shuddered a little and backed away from the hole, but Olie didn't notice.

"Well, let's go find Grandmaw," he said, leading the way out his front door.

Between his cabin and the lake lies a large, grassy area. At the shore were some boats pulled partly out of the water, a pier and a small log boathouse. He led us toward the lake across this yard, calling constantly, "Hi, Grandmaw! Come on, ye ol' honker! Here's someone wants t'see ye."

Grandmaw Honker didn't respond at once, though other creatures did. From under the cabin came a large cat named Tom and with him Nipper, a red fox. They crossed the lawn in a series of scuffles, the cat getting the worst of it. There was Peg Leg, a one-legged grackle whose life Olie had saved three years before and who returned to his homestead each spring. There were Maggy the pet crow, Pat the redheaded woodpecker and Joe the raven.

Olie greeted them all, tossing them tasty bits from a supply of food he always carried in his pocket. "Go on 'bout yer business," he grumbled. "I wasn't a-callin' you. I want Grandmaw. Where ye put her?"

He called for the Canadian goose again, but out of the brush came Big Foot, a huge snowshoe rabbit, and an assortment of chipmunks and squirrels. Sonya was in her glory. She gave her attention to one animal after another, emitting a constant flow of laughter and squeals of delight.

"Trouble with these critters is they don't have a lick o' sense," Warden Olie pretended to grumble as he gave Sonya some food to share with the animals. "All the books say a cat is supposed to kill chipmunks an' squirrels, an' look at old Tom. He jist wants to play with 'em. And that fox—he's jist plain dumb. Books say he feeds on birds like old Grandmaw, but he's jist plain crazy 'bout her. He go-'head and follows her round and sometimes I find 'em curled up asleep together. That's the whole trouble, these animals are ignorant. They never go-'head and read any books, so they don't know how to be animals."

Warden Olie straightened up and looked at us with a

strange squinting expression. I had seen him do this before and learned that what he spoke at such moments was
true and worth hearing.

"You folks go-'head and heard 'bout sech things as 'natural enemies' in the forest, an' instinctive killers. Let me
tell ye they ain't no sech thing. The cat ain't a killer till he's
taught it, likely 'nough by his maw; the wolf ain't a hunter
till he learns it. It's all a matter o' learnin', and if they
kin learn one thing, they kin learn another. Look—my
animals have learned to get 'long together ef they try.
Grandmaw!" he blurted impatiently, suddenly remembering the task of the moment. "Where are ye? Yer a-
gittin' more stubborn every day!"

"There she is," cried Sonya delightedly as a huge Canadian goose came walking from behind some brush near the
shore.

"Yep, it's Grandmaw," said Warden Olie. "But wait
a minute. Watch this. Ye kin see my two otters sunning
themselves on the pier."

The two animals were stretched out on their backs looking like miniature seals, apparently enjoying a lazy nap.

"Are they Mike and Ike?" asked Dorothy.

"Yep. Ye know 'em, don't you? Guess Sam and Giny
got you pretty well informed. Now watch Grandmaw.
She could never let anything go-'head and be that comfortable around here. If she sees 'em, you'll go-'head and
see some fun."

Grandmaw Honker saw the two otters all right. As
Warden Olie predicted, she couldn't tolerate such com-

fort. With her long neck outstretched, she waddled cautiously toward the sleeping Mike and Ike. When within reach of them she settled to the ground and studied the situation. Carefully she reached forward and touched Mike's leg with her beak. He jerked the leg away but didn't awaken. She did the same to Ike with a like result.

Warden Olie was chuckling softly as he watched. Back under his whiskers he kept saying in a half whisper, "Go-'head, go-'head, go-'head, go-'head-in-there," and Grandmaw went ahead. Suddenly she gave Mike a savage bite on his tail and quickly gave Ike the same treatment. The two otters, rudely startled out of their sweet dreams, fairly shot up into the air and into the water.

"Squawk!" went Grandmaw triumphantly, getting to her feet and waddling down the pier to the shore. The two otters swam about the surface of the lake, snorting and blowing, trying to figure out what had happened to them.

All of us were laughing, Warden Olie the loudest. "And folks wonder why I never get lonesome," he said. "Somethin' goin' on here all the time. Grandmaw has been comin' back every year for eight years. She broke a go-'head-in-there wing the first time and I fixed her up. She never forgets. Raised families for six years but not last year nor this. Too go-'head old, I guess. But she thinks she owns this place. She's boss here. Sometimes she's a little rough on people, but I just tell 'em if they don't like Grandmaw they can go away. She pesters the daylights out of Mike and Ike, but they like it."

Grandmaw Honker was now waddling up toward us, looking back in the direction of Mike and Ike occasionally. Warden Olie went to meet her. She pushed her head up against his hand and he scratched about in the feathers of her neck.

"Remember Sam and Giny, Grandmaw?" Warden Olie asked. "You saw them before. Easy now." Grandmaw took Giny's hand in her beak, and Warden Olie was concerned. "A goose can bite mighty hard if it takes a notion," he commented. "Easy now, Grandmaw."

Grandmaw was gentle but her very demeanor showed

she considered herself mistress of this place. She was especially cordial to Sonya. "Likes children," Warden Olie commented. "If I had a young'un I couldn't want a better nurse than Grandmaw. She's better 'n a watch dog."

Warden Olie was a keen observer of people as well as of animals. He looked sharply at Dorothy, who was watching Sonya and Grandmaw with obvious concern. Then in his usual blunt way he said, "You don't like animals, do you, lady?"

"Well," she answered hesitatingly, "I like them—that is, in a way. That is, I am learning to—I hope."

"Jist so's they don't go-'head and git too close, eh?" He laughed. "Well, I don't blame ye. Animals is jist no good. Look at this good-fer-nothin' goose. Someday I'll go-'head-in-there and tie that neck of hern in a bowknot!"

As he said this, he began handling the big goose in careless roughness. He ruffled the feathers of her neck, cupped his big hands about her head and shook it as if to break it off. Then he deliberately turned the big bird over on her back, scratching through her breast feathers and under her wings as if he meant to tear her to bits.

Grandmaw Honker squawked in loud protest, but she just loved it. The moment Olie stopped she got to her feet and came begging for more.

"See? What did I tell ye?" said Ollie, much out of breath. "She don't even know she's been abused. Thinks I'm jist playin' with her. Come here, ye varmint, I'll go-

'head and show you I mean it." He went after the delighted old bird like a wrestler, tumbling her about the ground even more roughly than before.

Finally he let Grandmaw get up on her feet and gave her some bits of food from his pocket. She gobbled them greedily. Olie gave us all some corn so we could feed the goose too. Even Dorothy joined the circle and seemed to be getting along well with the apparently docile bird.

Then I noticed that Warden Olie showed some worry. Grandmaw gently nipped at a bracelet Dorothy was wearing. "Easy now, Grandmaw," cautioned Warden Olie, walking over to her.

Grandmaw returned to the food in Dorothy's hand. "Look, Sam," said Dorothy a moment later, "how am I doing?" I looked and found that she was actually petting Grandmaw with one hand while she was feeding her with the other. She scratched among the feathers of the great bird's neck and stroked her head. "It's taking all the nerve I can muster," Dorothy said.

"I'm proud of you, dear," Dick said, and the three Ecks gathered about Grandmaw, showering affection on her.

"I was thinkin', you bein' a builder," Warden Olie broke in, "would you like to see some pitchers showin' the way we uster build things in old loggin' camps? I had the first camera in this country, and I took some things nobody else got."

Dick was interested and so were Giny, Sonya and I. We followed Warden Olie to his cabin. Dorothy stayed behind, still feeding Grandmaw. "I'll join you when Grandmaw has finished."

Warden Olie looked back at the big goose. "Easy now, Grandmaw. Remember what I say."

The old lumberjack's collection of pictures was remarkable indeed. The bunkhouses of the lumberjacks, the cook shack, the sleds piled high with logs, the log jams in rivers—he had them all. Some of the films were overexposed, the prints were badly faded, but still they were fascinating.

Then he began reminiscing about his early experiences. "It was tough in them days," he said, "but I wish I could go-'head through them again. No trucks then, no tractors, no good roads. When we went into camp it was to stay there all winter. We wouldn't see anyone but our own boys till the next spring. That camp was a world all our own and you made some mighty good friends. Once in a while there was a no-good amongst us, but mostly the boys was right. Then when the go-'head-in-there spring drive was on, when the logs went down the river— I tell ye nobody never saw more go-'head-in-there excitement."

"Listen," Giny broke in. "I think I heard a scream."

"I did too," Dick said anxiously. "Something happened to Dorothy."

We all rushed to the door. It was Dorothy all right. She was running in circles, screaming at the top of her voice. A few feet behind her was Grandmaw Honker yelling too and beating wildly with her wings. Even as we looked Dorothy made a frantic dash for the boathouse, ran in and slammed the door, Grandmaw ramming hard against it. Inside the boathouse we could still hear Dorothy screaming. Grandmaw Honker paced up and down in front of the door like a guardsman, apparently very much annoyed and upset.

Warden Olie was first to reach the scene of battle. "Grandmaw," he scolded, steering the ruffled goose to one side, "I'm ashamed of you. I told you to take it easy."

"She tried to kill me," Dorothy cried as Dick opened the door and brought her out. "She went right after my throat—after I'd been feeding her too."

"No, she didn't go after yer throat," said Warden Olie, still holding the goose. Grandmaw hadn't given up her goal and was peeking around his legs, looking for an opportunity to get at Dorothy again.

"But she did!" Dorothy insisted. "She reached right up and took a bite at me. I barely escaped."

"She wasn't after yer throat," Warden Olie said confidently. "It was yer necklace. Grandmaw has a go-'head weakness fer jewelry. She loves it. I saw her eyin' it when you fed her. Here, will this satisfy you, Grandmaw?"

He took from his pocket a string of sparkling, cheap beads and held them out to the excited goose. Immediately she snatched the beads in her beak and, with a little honk of satisfaction, she ran awkwardly away. A short distance off she dropped them on the ground, looked at them carefully, turned them over several times, then picked them up and carried them on.

"See? That's what she wanted," Warden Olie said triumphantly. "She's jist like all women, likes something to splurge with. Wasn't fair for you to have all them jewels you're a-wearin' and her none. She wasn't mad at you; jist wanted you to divide up."

We didn't see much more of Grandmaw that day. She was too much occupied with her necklace. She went walking back into the woods carrying her treasure and jabbering about it in goose language. Later we saw her swimming far out in the lake. Even as we watched, she took flight, looking like a plane as she circled high overhead.

Finally it was time for us to start home. Sonya was reluctant to leave, as we all were.

"Ye'll come again, won't ye?" asked Olie as we walked toward our car. "Grandmaw will be nicer to you next time, now that yer acquainted. And maybe you won't go-'head and get so fancied up," he said to Dorothy. "It's best not to tempt Grandmaw."

"I'll dress in sackcloth," Dorothy assured him.

"And bring my little Sonya here," demanded Olie, placing his arm about the child. "This young'un is mighty good with animals. Tell ye what I'll do," he said mysteriously. "If ye come back, I'll go-'head and show ye my big secret—somethin' I never showed another soul. Will ye?"

We promised to go-'head-in-there and come back—and that right soon. Grandmaw came sailing in just as we left, making a three-point landing near the pier, and bade us farewell with a squawk.

VII

A BATTLE IN THE NIGHT

UNEXPECTEDLY Giny and I were called to Chicago on business. We were gone a week. The city was in the throes of an unpleasant heat wave. Buildings and paved streets were like ovens, absorbing the heat in the daytime and holding it right through the night. Bathing beaches were crowded with people seeking relief. Traffic was noisy, tempers were short and courtesy was forgotten. We were grateful when the day came for us to return, and we left the city with a deep feeling of sympathy for those who must remain in it.

We arrived at home late, feeling that we had been away a long time. Our birds greeted us while we were crossing the lake in our canoe. Pestersome Pete swooped low over our heads, and if I understood his jabber rightly he was scolding us for having been away. The chickadees awaited us on the island. So did Blooey the old blue jay and a favorite pair of those cute little red-breasted nuthatches.

In the evening we paddled about in our canoe. Frogs and toads were in full voice, whippoorwills were calling from the forest depths, a hermit thrush sang his supreme song in the gathering gloom, a white-throated sparrow added his exotic melody, and a robin informed the world that his nest was filled with feathered miracles. Only one sour note spoiled the symphony. Giny Bubo was screaming forth his hunting call.

"Oh, I hoped he would be gone!" Giny exclaimed disappointedly. "Why can't he learn to eat grass? Then we could love him."

Bubo wasn't going to eat grass, that was sure. Right now he was searching the forest for his dinner, and grass didn't count.

We watched the graceful flight of a blue heron as he sailed into the sunset, and we could see him coast to a landing in the shallow waters among the stumps in West Bay. There he stood on his long stiltlike legs to do his evening fishing. We felt as if we knew this heron intimately. In early evenings and early mornings he came to this spot regularly.

We circled our lake, keeping close to the shore. We saw a deer, heard a porcupine gnawing and saw what we presumed was a muskrat swimming in the shallows.

Then suddenly the quiet of the night was broken by a strange cry.

"What in the world was that?" Giny asked.

"Something is in trouble in West Bay," I said, concerned. "That was a distress call."

We had not long to wait for the cry to be repeated. It was loud, brief, with desperation in it. The call came again and again, each time lessening in strength as if

some creature were losing a severe struggle. Then from the same spot in dark space came the voice of Giny Bubo.

"That tells it," I said, paddling forward. "That plagued owl is after the heron."

"The heron? Would he dare do that?" Giny questioned. "The heron is a terrific fighter himself and he's so large."

"He's a fighter, that's true. That long beak of his is like a spear, and he puts great power back of it. I've known of a heron driving off an attacking coyote. But the two birds are right together. Hear that?"

The distress call and the hunting call of Bubo came simultaneously and from the same direction. From the sound it seemed as if the battle was about over. We paddled toward the scene, but we were under a great handicap. I had forgotten my flashlight and ran the canoe into one stump after another. Giny, in the bow, was ducking under brush, but she urged me on.

The calls continued and yet there was no sound of a struggle. Really, despite all our experience in the forest and the assurance we have that man is safe there, it tested our courage to go into those black shadows. The terrifying cries, more intense as we neared the spot, suggested some unearthly creatures rather than the voices of birds.

All objects at water level were blacked out. We could see the shore trees silhouetted against the starlight, but our visibility was limited to things within ten feet about us. Giny and I sank to our knees in the canoe and turned the canoe around so I would go first. The cries now came from a point not more than fifty feet ahead of us. We moved on, purposely making noise with our paddles in the water and striking stumps, but the birds were so intent on each other they did not notice us. At last we were close enough to make out their forms dimly.

"The heron has been hurt!" Giny cried. "He's barely able to stand. Where is the owl?"

"There he is, on that upturned root to the right," I said. "Perhaps he's made one attack and is resting before another."

Even as I talked, the great owl spread his wings and swooped toward the injured heron. All my philosophy about predators deserted me at the moment. I stood up and struck at the owl with my paddle, using all my strength. The canoe lurched and nearly went over. My blow never reached Giny Bubo. With a marvelously quick movement he avoided it, and flew up with such power and grace I admired him in spite of everything.

The heron fluttered his wings desperately, but he was unable to fly.

"Can we do anything for him?" Giny asked anxiously.

"It's best to let him alone," I reasoned, out of breath from all the excitement. "If we try to follow him, he'll struggle and perhaps injure himself more. Let's move away a few feet and stand guard. I feel sure the owl won't return while we're here."

We worked our way through the stumps and then sat in silence. Beyond our range of vision in the darkness we could hear the heron move about occasionally.

"I never thought I'd be listening anxiously to hear that owl," Giny said, "but I wish I could hear him now. I'd know where he is."

It was fully a half hour before the call came. Then it was from a great distance. Bubo was not coming back. With this assurance we paddled farther away from the heron to free him from fear of our presence.

"Sam, listen. He's trying to fly." Giny drew my attention to the sound of wings.

"If he has strength to rise, I believe he'll do all right." I listened and looked into the night. "The heron struggles hard to begin his flight, but once on wing he flies easily."

There were more sounds of wings and water. Then to our delight we saw the long, angular form of the bird pass over us. He was unsteady at first but seemed to gain strength as he went. We could trace his flight against the stars for some distance. Then he gave forth one flat, gutteral call.

"He says 'I'm all right, thanks,'" Giny said with a sigh of relief.

After this experience we knew we could not rest until we had a look at Coony Castle. We stopped to get a flashlight and then paddled over to the mainland. The maple tree had a strange lonely appearance and the silence was foreboding as we approached. Andrea and her six babies were gone!

We searched the surrounding woods but did not find them, not even a track. There seemed to be a tone of sinister triumph in the final cry of Giny Bubo that came to us that night. My Giny looked at me with a question in her eyes that I did not dare answer.

VIII

MISSING IN ACTION

GINY pressed me for some hopeful thought about our family of raccoons. I tried my best to talk cheerfully, but our recent experience with the owl had a dark influence on my thinking.

"There comes a time when the raccoon mother takes her young out on hunting expeditions," I ventured. "Perhaps that's what has happened. She'd lead them about the forest and along the lake shore teaching them how to make a living. It's possible that she'd be gone many hours on such a trip."

"But isn't it probable that she'd come back home during the daytime?" Giny queried.

I had to admit that was likely. During daylight, then, we went to Coony Castle to see if it was occupied. It was not, and there was no recent evidence of raccoons coming and going.

"Surely the owl couldn't have destroyed them all." Giny was struggling against our fears. "Giny Bubo coudn't possibly eat so much."

"No, but unfortunately the great horned owl is one of the few creatures that will kill beyond its needs," I replied, not liking to dodge facts. "Anyway, let's not give up hope just because of that one possibility. Andrea may have outwitted Giny Bubo entirely."

Another day passed and still no trace of the raccoons. They were in our thoughts constantly. We had not realized how deeply this little family had become embedded in our hearts. Particularly Loony Coon haunted us with recollections of his funny ways.

The Eck family called one afternoon.

"Something happened that I must share with you," Dorothy said.

"It's the kind of thing that reveals how sweet and rich life really is," said the quiet-spoken Dick. Placing his arms around his daughter, he added, "And how loving our Sonya is."

Sonya, embarrassed, asked permission to feed the birds. While she went outside the cabin and called Pestersome Pete and the other birds, her parents told their story.

"Dorothy was much upset after our day at Warden Olie's place," Dick said.

"Yes—silly old me!" put in Dorothy. "I would have sold myself for a nickel and given back ten cents change."

"Indeed you were not silly, and if you're ever up for sale I'll buy you," Dick defended her. "We all know your problem about animals isn't make-believe. She isn't acting a part," he said to Giny and me. "She really suffers at times. We had quite a bad time over that day."

"Well, I still think I was silly."

"Bless you, Dorothy," said Giny, taking her hand. "You won't help matters by condemning yourself."

"She has plenty of courage," Dick said emphatically. "Well, anyway, we want you to hear the rest of the story. Sonya noticed that her mother was not quite herself, and——"

"You never saw a more solicitous person in your life," Dorothy broke in. "She just waited on me all the next day. I enjoyed it so much I let her drag it out as long as she would."

Both laughed. Then in bits of conversation that came partly from each they told their story.

Sonya had become very quiet during that evening. "She went to her room and was gone so long I went to see if anything was wrong," Dick said. "I found her praying, and I left without her knowing I'd been there."

Dorothy took up the thread of the story. "After a little while she came to me and asked if she might talk to me. She had been crying. Dick, you tell it. . . ." Dorothy could not trust her voice.

"Yes, I will, dear," he said. "Sonya had a hard time to get started, but at last she steadied herself and said, 'Mother, I've decided to give up animals.' We were both so surprised we couldn't think of a thing to say. 'Yes, Mother, I mean it,' she went on. 'I've been thinking and praying all day long for courage to tell you.' "

"Then I broke loose," Dorothy said. "I told her she'd do nothing of the sort. I said I knew animals meant more to her than anything else in the world."

"You should have heard the child," said Dick, beaming with paternal pride. "You'd have thought she was grown-up. She said, 'Yes, Mother, that's where I've been wrong. I've let them mean more to me than even you. Really, I didn't know you were so afraid of animals until we came here. I wouldn't make you unhappy for anything in the world. And so—well, you won't have to put up with any more turtles and snakes and things!' "

"She couldn't say any more," Dorothy broke in. "She just hugged me and buried her head in my shoulder."

"Bless her!" Dick smiled.

"Probably no one knows what a sacrifice she was making," I said, thinking what it would mean for me to give up my animal friends.

"Well, she *is* going to have animals!" Dorothy interrupted. "I told her so. I'll gather in turtles and snakes with my bare hands. I'll even pick up worms, *r-r-r-r-*" A shiver went over Dorothy that made her clench her fists and close her eyes.

"Mother!" cried Sonya, rushing in the door. "Pestersome Pete was sitting on my head!"

"Was he, dear?" Dorothy hugged her adopted daughter.

"Yes, and he lights on my nose and takes crumbs from my lips."

Dorothy looked at us with an expression of grim determination. "By the way, how is the family of raccoons getting along?"

We had hoped they might not ask about Andrea and her family, but now we were forced to explain our fears.

"Oh, no!" said Sonya, looking much distressed.

"You mean that old owl may have destroyed all of them?" Dorothy asked.

"Possibly, or if he got the best of Andrea, he may have picked off the little coons one at a time," I said.

"I can't bear to think of Loony Coon being carried off in the talons of that owl." Dorothy was leaning forward, eyes wide with excitement.

"Well, it could be, though we hope not."

"Why, we won't stand for it!" cried Dorothy, rising. "Let's search the woods and see if we find those coons. Let's——" Dorothy stopped abruptly, a look of surprise on her face. "Look at me!" she cried. "Look at me! I'm all concerned—all concerned about an animal. I never cared a hoot before whether animals came or went. Now I'm all bothered and anxious. I'm gaining—hurrah!"

We all echoed her *hurrah,* and Sonya's voice was loudest.

IX

THE LOST IS FOUND

WE SEARCHED thoroughly in the woods around Coony Castle, but we found no raccoons. I wasn't too surprised. Even if Andrea and her family were still around, we could easily have missed them. Looking for a raccoon in that big forest was about as simple as seeking the proverbial needle in a haystack.

In an attempt to cheer up Sonya, we promised her a campfire party, and presently came the evening chosen for the event. Nearly two weeks had passed since the disappearance of our raccoons. The long, warm evenings of July rested on the north country. The forest was teeming with life. The great bullfrog chorus which comes yearly from West Bay was at its peak of volume. Sundown brought an outburst of bird songs: linnets, grosbeaks, whippoorwills, thrushes, robins, song sparrows, white-throated and white-crowned sparrows.

The whippoorwill is a harmless and lovable bird who misrepresents himself. He cries a lot about beating poor William, but he doesn't mean it. Apparently he loves to hear his own voice, for he uses it so incessantly. It is a bit flattering to call his wail singing. Heard from afar, it blends beautifully with the forest choir, but as a solo voice, it has no music. Not many people have heard a whippoorwill at close range, and those who have are startled at the volume and sharpness of the call.

Dorothy Eck found this out. She and Giny were in our cabin kitchen preparing some things to take down to the campfire area for our dinner when a whippoorwill flew up and perched just outside the open kitchen window. They did not know he was there.

"Whippoorwill! Whippoorwill!" he cut loose, not more than eight feet from Dorothy's head.

"E-e-e-e-e-e-ek!" screamed Dorothy, jumping up in the air and dropping a bowl of salad on the floor. Lettuce, tomatoes, cucumbers, green peppers and gooey salad dressing went everywhere. "What kind of a beast is it? Close the windows and bolt the doors!"

"Just a whippoorwill. He won't hurt you." Giny laughed. The poor old bird, badly frightened, was half a mile away already.

"Oh," Dorothy groaned, "just look at what I've done! I'm terribly sorry."

"Don't be," Giny soothed her. "There's always one calamity with every campfire dinner. We have more salad materials in the refrigerator, and I'm sure we won't be attacked by another whippoorwill."

Giny called us all in so we could laugh about the incident and the mess. Then we cleaned it up and went to our campfire.

I often wonder at the fact that nature joys never grow tiresome. The charm of field and forest keeps pace with every step and stage of our growth. Since I was a child going to camps on the rivers of Illinois with my parents, I have known no pleasures equal to hiking, picnicking, campfire gatherings and learning about the outdoors.

A new kind of fun was in store for us this night of our first campfire party with the Ecks. Other friends had accepted our invitation. There were Ray and Ada, the forester and his wife who shared so many of our north-woods adventures, and several other neighbors who can reach our island from their cabins by boat.

Our dinner music was the forest symphony. Pestersome Pete was an uninvited guest and so were the chickadees. Chipmunks and squirrels came too. Sonya spent so much time feeding them she hardly ate anything herself. Everyone praised the food. What did it matter if some of it was overcooked, some of it actually burned? It didn't make any difference—anything cooked over a campfire tastes better.

Dinner over, we built up the fire and sat so we could look past the flames out across the lake. Daylight was fading and rich purple shadows settled on the forest. With binoculars we watched the flight of various birds at their evening feeding. Pestersome Pete and the chickadees delayed their bedtime to feed from Sonya's hand, but at last they retired into their hidden chambers for the night.

Then Ray, who has keen sight developed by years in the forest, discovered some sort of creature at the water's edge on the mainland at the nearest point to our island. He helped Sonya train a pair of binoculars on the spot.

"It's a raccoon!" the little girl cried delightedly.

"I believe it is," said Dick, studying the creature through his glasses.

Much excited, Giny took our own powerful glasses and, resting her arm against a tree, studied the creature at the distant shore.

"It is, Sam! It's a raccoon—a large one," she said. "Oh, could it be Andrea?"

"It's coming out into the lake," Sonya reported. "I believe it's going to swim. No, there it goes back."

"Up the bank into the brush," Giny carried on the story. "Something must have frightened it. I wonder if we dare hope."

For a few minutes there was no activity on the shore. Then Giny saw the animal again. "It's wading out into the water," she reported. "Now it's swimming!"

"Coming this way!" Dick exclaimed. "See the head and the V-shaped wake behind it?"

"Sam, there comes another one—a small one," Giny cried with renewed excitement. "I can see him right by the water's edge. He's timid. Now he wades out. He's swimming after the big one!"

"Another!" Ray exclaimed. "There are three in line now."

"Here comes another!" Sonya was so excited she was

trembling. We all got to our feet to watch the spectacle.
Binoculars were passed from one to another, though we
could now see with unaided eyes the ripples made by the
animals in the waters.

"Sam, there's another. That makes five, all coming
this way," said Giny, hardly able to control herself. "That
must be Andrea and her family. Wait—here comes the
sixth . . . and the seventh! I can see all seven."

Never would we forget that moment! The surface of
the lake was a glassy calm so that the V-shaped wakes of
the little swimmers could be easily discerned. Here they
came, seven of them, lined up like a flotilla of destroyers.
They remained evenly spaced, the larger one first and the

smaller ones following. The raccoon can travel great distances by water, but it takes him a long time to do it.

At my suggestion everyone in our party remained as quiet as possible. A land animal swimming is at disadvantage and knows it. Were we to move about and make noise, I had no doubt that the raccoons would turn and swim back.

Sonya was so excited she was about to pop, and Giny was too. The creatures came ashore near our campfire in back of some brush. Asking the others to wait, I took some pieces of bread and made my way down to meet them.

There was no doubt of it. Right behind Andrea came Loony Coon, the cub with the floppy left ear. The white streak on his head was more prominent than ever, now that he had a heavier coat of fur. Following his mother's lead, the youngster came up and, with very little evidence of timidity, nibbled at some bread. My heart was beating strongly with excitement and joy.

Andrea followed me as I went back up to our campfire. The cubs came too but more slowly. They were just a little shy.

"They're all here," Giny observed. "The owl didn't get them after all. Oh, you blessed creatures!"

Scraps from the table were literally showered on our unexpected guests. Several of them came right up to us for food, but others remained aloof and waited for us to toss them bites. Sonya hardly knew what she was doing, she was so thrilled. She was on her knees feeding Andrea, Loony Coon and one of his brothers all at once.

Andrea ate as if she were very hungry. But the cubs were soon satisfied, and then began playing, tumbling around, rolling over one another and keeping us all in laughter.

"Where do you suppose they've been?" Giny asked.

"I can only guess," I replied. "But I would suppose Andrea moved her family when she knew the owl had discovered their nest. Then as soon as the cubs' eyes were open, she began training them to hunt. No doubt they've found another tree for a home or perhaps space under a cabin. As soon as they were large enough to swim she brought them over here—just as she has her families of other years."

"E-e-e-e-e-ek!" Dorothy screamed suddenly. The raccoons scattered into the brush.

"What's the matter?" Dick asked.

"That little one—the one with the floppy ear—he bit me!" she exclaimed.

"Bit you?"

"Yes, he bit my toe!"

Dorothy was wearing toeless shoes and heavy red socks. Her big toe was too much of a temptation for Loony Coon. I saw him eying the toe longingly. A moment later when the attention of the party was directed elsewhere he sneaked up and took another quick nip. It was a playful bite that did not cut the flesh, but it brought a new "E-e-e-e-e-ek" from Dorothy.

"Mother," Sonya said appealingly, "Loony Coon is having such a good time. Couldn't you let him bite your toe just a little? He wants to so badly! And wouldn't it prove you're glad he's back if you put your foot out where he can reach it?"

She did—and he did!

X

THE KILLER STRIKES

ANDREA and her *circus*—as we began calling this family of raccoons—came nightly after this first visit. However, we seldom saw them swimming. I sat one twilight after another with my movie camera ready to catch them, but never did I record the scene. Only after daylight had faded to the point where pictures could not be taken did they come, making their V-shaped wakes through glossy, gray waters. Other times they came well after dark.

Our concern for their safety was very great now. The six cubs were still small enough to tempt Giny Bubo. The little ones were becoming increasingly bold and often wandered away from Andrea to play and hunt. They were much more open to the owl's observation and attack. We heard Giny Bubo's eerie call every night. All too frequently it came from the direction Andrea and her family must follow on their nightly journey to the island.

"How soon will the cubs be so large that Bubo will let them alone?" Giny asked one night.

"I believe if they escape him for two or three more weeks they're safe," I reasoned. "They're growing rapidly and learning to defend themselves. Remember Olie's remark—that animal development is more education than instinct. Just notice how Andrea is teaching her babies all the tricks that make the raccoon such a respected creature."

That evening we saw more of this educational process. The circus had already landed on the island. Giny discovered them on the trail that leads from our campsite to the cabin.

"Here they come," Giny announced and switched on the floodlights to illuminate our yard. "Andrea is first and there's Loony Coon right beside her. He's mother's pet all right."

It was apparent from the first that Loony Coon was Andrea's favorite of the entire family, and she his. Not that she neglected to train any of them. But while the other five cubs played with one another and loped about the forest independently, Loony Coon stayed close to Andrea. They ran together, fed together and played together.

I was in another part of the house that evening, but I hurried when Giny called.

"Sam, you missed something!" she exclaimed. "Andrea turned a somersault." She laughed. "Watch, maybe she'll do it again. Loony Coon hid behind a little balsam tree, and when she came along he jumped at her. She turned a complete flip and landed on her back."

Loony Coon was scuffling with her and, of course, getting the worst of it. At the end of this round Andrea had him pinned to earth with her front feet the way she holds down a captured frog. Loony Coon was struggling and making a little chattering noise, likely the raccoon for "let me go." Andrea held him longer, nipping him here and there until he ceased struggling. Then she released him. Back into the brush he ran in that funny lope of his.

We stayed at the window and watched.

"Look! Look!" I nudged Giny. "Here he comes again."

The young cub came out of the brush, creeping stealthily as a cat. Andrea had gone to the pan of food we'd left for her and was just about to settle down to a quiet meal. Suddenly Loony Coon rushed and jumped at her face. We saw again her ability as an acrobat. Catching the spirit of play, she warded off Loony Coon's blow, then turned a forward somersault *in the air,* landing on her back. Loony Coon tried biting at her throat, but quickly her strong paws put him in his place—which was flat on the ground. The other cubs, with or without invitation, now joined the battle. For a few minutes there were raccoons all over the yard, scratching, biting, wrestling, squealing, growling. Then the battle royal ended as suddenly as it had started and everyone settled down to dinner.

"Do you notice," I said to Giny, "that Andrea never actually gives them anything to eat? In fact, she snatches food away from them if she can. Here, I'll show you what I mean."

I tossed a single peanut near Andrea. Now, of all food the peanut is the favorite with raccoons. The very sound of a peanut falling will attract their attention from anything else. When this peanut hit the ground the entire family made a grab for it. Andrea, stronger and quicker than her cubs, reached it first and not even Loony Coon could get a single bite from her.

"Why, Andrea!" exclaimed Giny. "I'm surprised. That's no way for a mother to act. You should share with your babies."

"No. They must learn that in the forest, it's first come first served," I commented. "Animals have to grab their food, even fight for it, before it gets away. A frog, a toad or a mouse won't come and offer himself to these fellows. They must learn to catch things quickly. By her example she's training them for practical living."

"I suppose so." Giny was disappointed. "Couldn't she wait until they're a little older to be so practical?"

"There isn't much time for babyhood in the forest," I replied. "Owls and other predators won't wait."

"But look at them now," Giny broke in.

Andrea and Loony Coon had begun a strange little raccoon habit we call *wuzzling*. As if by preagreement they had placed themselves beside each other, head to tail, and each was chewing in the middle of the other's back. It was a clear case of "you scratch my back and I'll scratch yours." No doubt it affords each a measure of pleasure and loosens summer fur which will soon be exchanged for heavier winter coats. This *wuzzling* would continue for ten or fifteen minutes, with the coons changing position often. Sometimes Loony Coon and Andrea chewed at each other's throat fur, sometimes in that difficult spot for an individual to reach at the base of the tail. But each wuzzled the same area on the other.

Giny and I went outside with a supply of peanuts and sat on the front steps. The raccoons gathered about us. To cultivate their friendships, we presented peanuts to each one personally. Occasionally we gave them small bites of marshmallow, another favorite food, but we limited the amount, for sweets are not too good for animals. The little fellows climbed all over us.

"Apparently Andrea has trained them to be unafraid of us," Giny said.

"How often we have seen that," I commented. "When any kind of animal has been friendly with us, this friendliness is communicated in some degree to the children. I believe, though, that all youngsters are naturally friendly."

We made our first motion pictures of the family that night using floodlights. Loony Coon seemed cut out for a movie career. It was he who struck the unusual pose and did the unusual thing in every scene.

"What a ham we have in that little fellow!" Giny declared. "Look how he sits up and poses when the lights go on. He's vain, camera-conscious, that's what he is. That youngster is headed for Hollywood."

He was an actor all right, but with a streak of the clown. While we were in the house for a few moments we left the camera on the tripod out in the yard. Loony Coon climbed up on it and wiped his dirty feet on the lenses, then stepped on the trigger release and ran off one hundred feet of film with the camera pointed at nothing but the ground.

We photographed all the family that night, and it was a good thing we did. We never saw all seven together again. The next night when they returned there were only Andrea and five cubs. Giny Bubo's cry had a tone of contentment and triumph.

XI

PRIVATE ENEMY NUMBER ONE

ANDREA and her family were not the only raccoons who came to our island as the summer advanced. Each night the number increased. Some of them we knew from previous years and could identify by a marking or mannerism. It was always a thrilling moment when one of our friends returned.

"Sam, look who's here!" Giny called late one night as she took a last look at the feeding area before turning off the floodlight.

"Another wanderer returned?" I asked, coming beside her to look out the window.

"It's Big Boy, and he's positively enormous."

"The largest of them all," I said. "In fact, he's the largest raccoon I have ever known—and one of the handsomest. His hair looks as if he made regular trips to the beauty parlor. But look at Loony Coon!"

Our favorite little cub was advancing toward the huge coon belligerently. They were about as evenly matched as a chipmunk ready to attack a bear. But Loony Coon meant business, and he had the support of the rest of his family. With a snarl and a snap he flew at Big Boy, and after him came his four brothers and sisters in one wild concerted charge. Big Boy vanished into the brush as if a wind had blown him away.

"Why would he run?" Giny asked. "He could swallow one of them with a single gulp."

"Another mystery in raccoonology," I commented. "Big Boy is a male. Like the male bear, the daddy raccoon is not welcome around youngsters. Sometimes they kill and eat their own offspring. Just why he runs from the little ones I don't know. Maybe it's because Andrea is so close at hand. Look, here he comes again!"

Longing for the food which was there in such tempting abundance, Big Boy came peeking out from under a balsam tree. He eyed the cubs, who greeted him with a growl. Then a step at a time he began edging toward a dish. He never reached it. This time it was Andrea who took out after him, and all the cubs followed. With a snarl she charged, and he promptly took to flight. A long chase followed. We could hear them going through the brush, Andrea snarling, the cubs making a peculiar little whining noise. Big Boy needed all his breath to get away.

"Why is she so mean to him?" Giny asked in sympathy. "There's plenty of food for all. It wouldn't hurt Andrea to let him have a little."

"I think I know," I replied. "From the way she treats him, Big Boy must be Andrea's husband."

"Is that so?" Giny challenged. "Is that the way wives

are supposed to treat husbands?" She looked at me as
if I might be the next one chased through the underbrush.

"Now, now, don't jump to conclusions," I protested.
I mean only *raccoon* husbands. At certain times they're
just about as welcome as a calamity. You notice that
Andrea doesn't let any of the adult coons come near her
young. But it's only Big Boy whom she treats so savagely.
It's pretty good evidence that he's the father."

After a while Andrea and her tribe returned from the chase and monopolized all the feeding pans. Big Boy came close enough to peer out from the brush, but he didn't attempt to join the dinner party.

"Andrea, shame on you!" Giny scolded. "Didn't you promise to love, honor and obey your husband—or at least to love and honor? Let him have some food."

But Andrea just looked daggers at Big Boy and bared her teeth to show him what would happen if he came closer.

"If raccoons have a doghouse, he's certainly in it," I concluded.

In the middle of the night I heard a noise at the feeding pans. I slipped into a robe and went to the window where I could see what was going on. There was Big Boy eating his fill with no competition whatever. Andrea and her circus had gone home.

Another exciting evening was when a second family of raccoons came to the island.

"It's Lady!" cried Giny joyously. "Lady's come back— and she has a family of three."

I felt like giving a cheer. Lady had come to us now for three years. She was quite different from Andrea in appearance and manners.

"See," Giny enthused, "no one could mistake that very black coat and the way she walks with such dignity and grace. Yes, it's Lady."

But if we welcomed her Andrea did not. There was a brief scuffle in which Andrea learned that Lady had no notion of retreating. Loony Coon advanced toward one of the new youngsters as if he meant to do battle, but he got his face slapped too. Then Lady and her family took one feeding pan while Andrea and Company took another, and everyone was happy.

Other raccoon families joined the nightly gathering. How word gets about among these forest creatures no one can say, but certainly something, someway, was advertising the fact that there were good food and good service for coons on Campbells' island.

One evening after the mob had arrived, Giny stood at our doorway counting them. "If they'd only stand still for a moment I could do this more accurately," she said. "There are eighteen right here at the step. Here come three more out of the brush, that's twenty-one. There are two more, twenty-three—and two coming down a tree. Sam, come and see this spectacle. We have twenty-five raccoons here at one time."

I went to her and looked out. For the moment an armistice was declared in the raccoon ranks and they all stood still looking up at us. We had not yet placed food out for them and they were asking for it.

"Anyone who hasn't seen twenty-five raccoons at one time has missed something," I said. "Twenty-five pairs of eyes looking at us, twenty-five noses all pointed at the same angle, twenty-five masked faces—surely this *is* a sight."

I withheld their food purposely until I could record this occasion with my camera. When at last dinner was placed before them, the armistice was off. Squabbling broke out all over the area. Their savage snarls sounded as if they were tearing one another to pieces. However, no one gets hurt in these brawls and in the end each gets his share of food.

Still later this same evening the twenty-sixth raccoon joined the parade. It was the one we had named *Blondy* because of his very light-colored fur. We had been watching anxiously for Blondy. A year before he was our favorite cub, having the same temperament as Loony Coon. We were much attached to him and wondered why he did not return.

Giny and I were in another part of the house when Blondy announced his arrival. He always has had the cutest way of pulling our screen door to pieces! In the first season we had Blondy I spent half my time repairing that door. Hence, when we heard the familiar ripping of screen and the splintering of wood, we went on the run.

"Blondy," we both cried at once, "you have come back to us!"

We opened the door and Blondy came in. He rose on his hind legs and reached up to us just as he had when he was a cub. Then Giny and I saw something that wiped the smiles off our faces. Blondy had lost half of his left front leg, and a pitiful little stub extended toward us.

"Blondy," Giny said much distressed, "Blondy, how did that happen?"

"A steel trap!" I declared. "Blondy, old pal, did you get caught in one of those awful things?"

The answer was obvious. His condition was testimony to the cruelty involved in this way of capturing animals. His wound was healed now. Doubtless during a warm spell in the winter he had awakened, gone wandering in search of food and fallen victim to the merciless steel jaws which trappers place about the forest. Then followed long hours of indescribable suffering before his leg broke off, or perhaps he chewed it off with his own teeth, and he hobbled away.

Giny could not restrain her tears. "When *will* people stop torturing creatures like that?" she asked.

"Someday when we learn that we harm ourselves most when we are cruel to others," I answered sadly. "It's an old, old problem. Blondy is only one of millions to suffer that way. Someday men's spiritual growth will reach the point of discarding such methods, I feel sure—but not soon."

If Blondy knew that human hands set the trap that crippled him, he did not hold it against us. He was friendly as ever. We went out and sat on the front steps to be with him. He crawled into our laps and searched in our pockets for especially tasty bites of food, just as he had a year before. He was so happy that our sorrow vanished. We noted that seldom did any of the other coons quarrel with him. Whether this was consideration for his handicap or respect for his prowess, we do not know.

One day the Eck family came to the island in great excitement. Sonya started trying to tell us a story about something or other before the boat touched the land.

"Oh-h-h-h, guess what happened? Guess what happened?" she cried, running to us as soon as she could get ashore. Her parents followed, no less excited than she.

"My goodness, what *has* happened?" Giny asked, as we went to meet our guests. "It must be something wonderful."

"Oh, it *is* wonderful," cried Sonya, rushing into her arms. "Shall I tell them, Mother?"

"Well, someone tell us!" I exclaimed. "We're bursting with curiosity."

"They came!" Sonya cried. "They came right to our cabin and we had them all to ourselves."

"That's right," Dick Eck said. "They came to us all right."

"Who came?" I asked, puzzled.

"Why, the raccoons," said Sonya.

"Yes, to be sure," Dorothy said. "Raccoons are the only animals in the world right now. You should know who came without asking."

"Was it our Andrea and her cubs?" asked Giny, laughing and hugging the thrilled Sonya.

"Yes," said the child, giggling with delight. "Loony Coon was there. We knew him at once—with his floppy ear and white streak on his head."

"Yes, he was the scoundrel who did it," Dick put in.

"Did what?"

"Well, let me tell this part," Dorothy said with a crooked smile. "You know Dick, like most husbands, likes apple pie. It's a passion of his. He would eat apple pie three times a day if he had the chance. Well, I made him an apple pie." She paused and looked at the other two, who were holding back laughter. "I made it extra thick, the way he likes it. It was near dinnertime when the pie was finished, and since he likes his pie cold I put it on the back-porch railing to cool. . . ."

"May I tell the next part?" Dick broke in. "I'm the one who saw it. I heard a noise on the back porch and looked out to see a raccoon up on the railing, just approaching that pie." He was interrupted by a flow of giggles from Sonya. "I moved fast, but not fast enough. The coon stepped right into the pie and both he and it went in a tumble to the porch floor."

"Poor Loony Coon," Sonya said.

"Poor Loony Coon? How about my pie?" her father asked.

"And how about all my hard work?" Dorothy sought sympathy too.

"Poor Loony Coon!" repeated Sonya. "It got all over him."

"We all rushed to the door," Dorothy said. "Oh, what a mess! The pie fell upside down right on top of Loony Coon. It smeared him and splashed all over the porch."

"Mother should have baked two pies," Sonya declared, her eyes dancing.

"One for your father?" I asked.

"No, both for the raccoons." The child laughed. "They all came and there wasn't enough."

"Next time I'll do better," Dorothy grumbled. "Of course I haven't a thing else to do but bake pies for raccoons."

Finally we learned the rest of the story. The raccoons had spent much of the evening with the Ecks and had eaten not only the pie but every other bit of sweet in the house.

"That gives us some idea of how far raccoons travel," I remarked. "The shortest route to your cabin must be at least two miles. It seems a long way for these little animals to go, and yet I've known them to cover even greater distances."

"But, Mr. Campbell," said Sonya, sobering, "there were only four of the little ones. We looked for the other two all over and couldn't find them."

Giny looked distressed.

"Could it be the owl?" Dorothy asked.

I nodded reluctantly. "There are other enemies who might kill young raccoons," I said. "But we know the owl is in this area and we know he has definitely spotted this family. It is characteristic of the bird to concentrate his hunting that way—even until he has done away with them all."

"Something *must* be done!" Giny declared determinedly. "Why, we can't idly watch Andrea's family disappear one by one. Let's do something about it."

But what we could do was still a question.

XII

HORS DE COMBAT

THE Ecks and Campbells held a combined indignation meeting and council of war.

"If Giny Bubo could hear us plotting against him, he'd leave the country," Giny said.

"Or else laugh his feathers off at our funny ideas," put in Dorothy.

We had suggested everything from making a pet of him to serving him an individual atomic bomb. No idea seemed to offer much hope.

"How would it be to cage up Andrea and her cubs until they are larger?" Dick suggested seriously.

"That would be pretty hard to do," I said. "Anyway, it's not just Andrea's family that concerns us. There are many other raccoons in the woods and we couldn't catch them all."

There was silence in the group. Then Sonya said, "Could we take turns watching for the owl? I'd be glad to stay up all night and guard the raccoons. I'd——"

"No, dear," I interrupted. "It wouldn't do any good. We could guard so little of these big woods, and the raccoons and the owl wander far and wide."

Silence again. Then Giny had an idea. "Could we catch Giny Bubo alive and take him to a zoo?"

This seemed to have a thread of possibility. A live trap for an owl might be designed.

"We must remember, though," I cautioned them, "this is a legal game refuge and we have no right to trap anything or to shoot it. Only the conservation warden can take such steps."

It was agreed that I should place the whole matter before the warden and ask his help. Every night now was a serious threat to our pets, and our hopes were dimmed when I called at the warden's home and found that he was away on other work and would not return for a week or more.

Giny Bubo perched right on our island that evening and repeatedly gave his catlike cries. He seemed to be deliberately showing his contempt for us. I went to his tree and frightened him away. He merely flew to the mainland and recommenced his ominous call.

"It looks as though he has us whipped," I said to Giny. "I've run out of ideas."

"Listen!" cried Giny. "What's that?"

Out of the blackness on the mainland came a series of fierce savage animal cries. The sounds were from a swampy area where it would be just about impossible for us to go at night. For several minutes we listened anxiously.

"There's a terrible fight going on!" Giny exclaimed. "I wish there were something we could do to stop it."

But then there was deep silence.

"It's over," I said.

That evening we watched most anxiously for Andrea. Big Boy showed up and had the feeding station all to himself. Blondy joined Big Boy and they were right friendly with each other. Later Lady came with her three cubs. Still no Andrea . . .

Near midnight Giny stood at the window while I was reading. Suddenly she gave a little gasp. "She's here, Sam," she said, "and . . . oh, just look at her! She's been in a terrible fight, I do believe. Her face is cut and she seems unable to walk steadily."

Andrea indeed was a sorry sight. She bore the evidence of a savage struggle. There were deep gashes in her face and about her head, and her fur was disheveled.

"And there's Loony Coon," cried Giny. "Sam, he's been hurt too. That must have been their fight we heard. What has happened?"

Loony Coon showed some wounds but he was as energetic as ever. He raced up to the feeding pan and immediately got in a rough-and-tumble match with his brothers. Andrea, however, was not interested in food. She walked over to the birdbath and with great difficulty raised herself up on her hind feet so she could reach in. Then she drank and drank as though she could never get enough.

Giny hurriedly prepared some warm bread and milk. Andrea ate sparingly of this, then curled up on the

ground. Apparently she had been through a most trying
and exhausting experience.

"Do you notice that we don't hear the voice of Giny
Bubo?" I asked Giny.

We listened for a time, fearful lest the weird hunting
cry of the owl would pierce the solitude. Yet only the
sounds of wind in the pines and the voices of insects, frogs,
tree toads and night birds came to us.

I knelt beside Andrea and examined her wounds. They
were numerous but none of them was serious. There were
sharp gashes in the flesh, and I could see many spots on
her body where large chunks of fur had been snatched
from her coat. About her eyes were cuts and her lips
were lacerated.

"It looks to me as if Andrea has settled accounts," I
said to Giny as I rose to my feet. "These wounds were
made by sharp talons and a powerful beak, not by the
fangs of a wolf or coyote. It's my guess that Giny Bubo
made a mistake tonight, a fatal one for him. It may be
that he got overconfident. This time I believe he struck
at Loony Coon. Perhaps Andrea was in the near-by
brush and the owl didn't see her. Giny Bubo had courage, strength and cleverness, but Andrea had all this and
one thing more—the determination to defend her young.
Yes, I believe Andrea and Giny Bubo fought it out tonight."

Giny brought out more warm milk for Andrea and
knelt near her as she ate it. "Bless you, Andrea," she
said. "Raising a family in a forest is difficult, isn't it?"

The next day we went through the woods in the direction from which the sounds of combat had come the night before. After considerable searching we found grim evidence of the battle, right at the edge of the swampy area. Owl wings and feathers were scattered about. The ground was torn up and brush was tangled and broken. "To the victor belongs the spoils." No doubt Andrea and her cubs had feasted on fresh great horned owl when the struggle was over.

The voice of Giny Bubo was not heard again in our forest.

XIII

GRANDMAW ON THE WARPATH

WARDEN OLIE was impatient. "It's high time you folks get back here," he wrote. "I been watching fer word from you every day. Are you so messed up with them raccoons that you fergit yor other friends? Grandmaw Honker wants you so come along—and if you come without Sonya I'll send you back. I sure fell for that young'un."

So it wasn't long until we were on our merry way to Warden Olie's cabin camp with the Ecks—merry, that is, all except for Dorothy.

"Do you suppose Grandmaw will remember me?" she worried. "I haven't a single piece of jewelry on today, except my wedding ring. Surely Grandmaw wouldn't want that."

The warden wasn't at home when we arrived, but we found him in the midst of a young riot at the next cabin beyond. Four irate women stood facing him, waving their arms wildly, all talking at once.

It was clear that Olie was having his troubles. Grandmaw Honker, just behind him, was trying constantly to get around him to the left, or the right, or through his legs toward the quartet of ladies. One moment Olie gestured and talked to the women, the next he had to catch

Grandmaw and pull her back, and the next he held his hands to his ears to shut out the wild ranting and screaming.

"What's going on?" Giny asked as we watched the scene from the car. "Those ladies are angry."

"That's putting it mildly," I replied as there was a new outburst of yelling and arm waving from the group. "If I'm not mistaken, Grandmaw Honker is in trouble, or at least she's stirred up some."

We could hear Olie's voice now rising above the storm. "Wait a minute! Wait a minute!" he yelled. Grandmaw sneaked around his right side and he grabbed her and pulled her back. Then she went around the left side and he barely caught her in time. Then he got straddle of her and held her tightly between his legs. "Here, go-'head-in-there and take this!" we heard him shout. He drew some money from his pocket and gave it to the women. They took it in a snatchy sort of way and, throwing a few more vocal volleys at him, went inside the cabin.

Olie busied himself with Grandmaw. A moment later the four ladies burst out of the cabin, suitcases in hand, and with tempers unsubdued. They got into their car which stood near by, slammed the doors so hard it sounded like four gunshots and drove by us with their engine roaring in low, too mad even to shift the gears. As they passed our car one of the four rolled down a window and called back at Olie, "And we're *never* coming back, understand?"

At this point Grandmaw broke loose from Olie. With wings slapping the ground she took out after the car, squawking in goose fashion. The departing ladies then shifted into high gear and sped down the road.

Warden Olie saw us now and came forward, mopping his brow. "Howdy, folks," he said as we piled out of the car. "Mighty glad to see you. Ye got here in time to see the commotion, didn't ye?" He greeted us all, cast an approving glance at Dorothy's attire and took the willing Sonya in his long arms. "I been mighty lonesome for this tyke since ye left. Grandmaw has been askin' fer ye in her own honkin' way."

Grandmaw had given up the chase and turned her attention to Olie's cat, asleep on the back steps of his cabin. Right that moment the old goose was approaching the cat, slowly, her long neck arched low. We all watched in silence. Nearer and nearer she stretched and stretched until she gave the cat's tail a good nip. "Miaow!" screamed the cat and jumped right up in the air. Then she looked reproachfully at the goose and her tail switched ominously. Grandmaw strutted away looking for more worlds to disturb.

"Now, Olie, what was going on?" I asked. "We thought we might have to come to your rescue."

"Well, guess I can't blame the ladies for bein' mad, really." He stroked his whiskers and looked at Grandmaw, who was just disappearing around the house. "Ye see, Grandmaw Honker had one o' her bad days. She

don't aim to cause trouble—she jist can't control herself."
He stared after the goose and then he looked over to the
cabin where the scene had taken place.

"Those go-'head ladies writ up and reserved a cabin,"
he went on. "Wanted to stay all this month. Said they
liked animals, an' heerd they could see lots of 'em here.
Well, I go-'head-in-there an' fixed up my best cabin fer
'em and in they moved. That was last night. Everything
seemed all right at fust. I saw them down by the lake this
mornin', lookin' at the sunrise. Heerd 'em talkin' to
Grandmaw, and they was all a-laughin'. So I goes to town
fer supplies. Phew!" Olie wiped his brow at his recollections.

"Guess I stayed longer 'n I should," he went on. "Got
to talkin' to my buddies an' time slipped by so's I jist got
back half hour ago. And, oh—go-'head, go-'head, go-
'head . . ." He said these go-'heads with gestures. First
he held his head in his hands, then waved both arms in
helplessness.

"I heard women screamin' at me before I got out of
my jalopy," Olie continued. "I looked at their cabin, an'
I wish ye coulda seen what I saw. Aw, go-'head-in-
there . . ." He broke out laughing and so did we. "Here
was Grandmaw, struttin' up and down like a guard at
Buckin'ham Palace. She was so wrought-up she was a-
draggin' her wings like when she goes into a fight. Jist
inside the front porch, 'fraid t' open the screen door, was
them four ladies—all screamin' at me to go-'head an'

save 'em." Warden Olie broke into a laugh that doubled
him up.

"What happened, Olie?" asked Dorothy. His merri-
ment was infectious. We were all straining for his full
story.

"I don't know everythin' that went on before I got
there," Olie said. "Mebbe it's jist as good I don't. As it
is, they threaten to go-'head an' sue me. Well, I went
over to their cabin, feelin' like I was walkin' into a trap.
Grandmaw was so riled up she hardly spoke to me. She
was a-tryin' to git at them women in that porch. The
ladies was all talkin' at once so I couldn't git ever'thing
they said, but it seems that soon after I left fer town, one
of the ladies went outdoors. She was a-wearin' a red
bracelet."

Dorothy nodded understandingly.

"Yep, yer gettin' the idea." Warden Olie chuckled.
"The ladies had been gittin' along right good with Grandmaw, so they felt kinda confident. But Grandmaw was
taken with that bracelet, and she starts in that cute way
of hern t' git it. The lady who was a-wearin' it didn't
want to give it up. Ye know—sorta selfish. So Grandmaw took matters in her own hands."

"I know only too well," Dorothy said.

"Yep—" Olie looked at her, his eyes twinkling—"but
you was decent 'bout it. These ladies go-'head-in-there
and got four hunks o' firewood and set in to fight Grandmaw. One o' the ladies hurls a hunk o' wood at Grandmaw,

but her aim warn't good and she hits another lady right on her pet corn. Anyway they did a lot of yelpin' and Grandmaw's never been use' ter such carryin' on. So she got in a huff and sailed into all four of 'em. Go-'head-in-there! I'd a-give my best boots ter see it." Olie was holding his sides. "Grandmaw disarmed 'em in a hurry. The four hunks o' wood are right there now where the women threw them, and then they retreated double-time into the cabin. There the old gals stayed, with Grandmaw struttin' up and down darin' any one or all of 'em to go-'head and come out and fight."

Warden Olie was laughing so hard he could hardly talk, and so were we.

"Well, they should have been glad," Giny finally managed to say. "No one was hurt and you came to their rescue."

"Nope, nothin' hurt 'cept the ladies' feelin's and Grandmaw's pride," the big woodsman went on. "I came, but I didn't come jist as soon as the ladies thought I shoulda. Grandmaw Honker locked 'em up 'long 'bout nine o'clock in the mornin'. I didn't go-'head an' git back till two in the afternoon. She had 'em in that cabin fer five hours! An' they'd be there yet if I hadn't come. Well, I gave 'em back all their rent, an' now they can go someplace where no goose will bother 'em. Look!"

He directed our attention to the guest cabin. There was Grandmaw looking angrily at the screen porch that had so recently been a prison. Sticking her long neck out, she gave one prolonged loud hiss—and strutted on.

"Did you hear what the ladies said to you when they left?" Dick asked.

"No, couldn't make out anything they said," Olie answered.

"One called, 'And we're *never* coming back.'"

"Well," said Olie with a twinkle and a wink, "that will be soon enough fer Grandmaw and me."

We had a wonderful afternoon at Warden Olie's Sanctuary. His animals were in fine form. Grandmaw Honker came back, her disposition entirely mended. She recognized Dorothy. Deliberately the goose looked on her wrist for bracelets, on her throat for a necklace and at her ears for earrings. Finding none, she accepted some corn from Dorothy's fingers and all was forgotten and forgiven. The goose took to following Sonya, much to her delight. "If you was around here much," Olie said to her parents, "pretty soon you'd have to ask Grandmaw's permission to go near yer own daughter."

Mike and Ike the otters put on a show for us. After asking us to stay back so there would not be too many people, Olie led Sonya out on his pier where the two otters were sun-bathing. He had her sit with her feet hanging down from the pier and he sat beside her. As soon as the two were seated, Mike and Ike half slid, half walked right into their laps. Sonya squealed with obvious delight.

"She likes ye, Sonya," said Olie. "Mike's a wonderful animal—always in good humor, never gets upset, 'cept when Grandmaw bites her tail."

"Are they fisheaters?" Dick asked as we walked out to them on Olie's invitation.

"Mebbe sometimes otters might eat fish," Olie said. "But not often. Matter o' fact, the otter is one o' the best friends fish have. He eats crawfish, and crawfish destroy lots o' fish, an' the otter eats frogs an' bloodsuckers an' even turtles—all enemies of fish." He patted Ike, who was affectionately pushing her nose into his whiskers. "Otters should be more appreciated by men—they're all on our side."

"Is this what you meant, Mr. Olie, when you said you would show us something we wouldn't believe?" Sonya looked as if her fondest dream had already come true as she petted these slender, graceful animals.

"I guess I did go-'head an' promise that, didn't I?" Olie smiled at her. "I wondered if you'd remember. Nope—had somethin' else in mind. I'll show ye, if we kin git rid of these scamps. Come, Mike and Ike—go fer a swim before Grandmaw gits ye." The two otters reluctantly left the laps of Sonya and Olie and plunged into the water. Swimming gracefully, they disappeared down the shore line.

Now we all watched Olie to see what was the big surprise he had for us—that thing which we wouldn't believe. He enjoyed keeping us mystified. "Ye won't believe it, I tell ye, and nobody'll believe it when ye tell it," he said.

He asked us to stay at the base of the pier, and walked to the end. Here he gave a prolonged whistle, followed by a call, "Oh-ho, Jim. Come, Jim." Our curiosity aroused, we watched the surface of the water and the sky overhead to see what would answer this summons. Again and again Olie gave the whistle and the call. Presently he said, "Here he comes—go-'head an' get ready, folks."

We hadn't seen a living thing as yet, but Olie insisted, "He's comin'." Out toward the center of the lake I saw a swirl in the water such as a fish makes when it leaps. Olie called again, then reached down into a tin can and took out a few worms. "Watch close, folks," he called. "This show won't last long."

He tossed several worms into the water beside the pier. To my utter amazement I saw the form of a huge fish come and get them. "Would you believe it!" Giny exclaimed. "What kind of a fish is it?"

"A muskellunge!" I declared.

Olie was reaching down from the pier toward the water, holding some worms in his fingers. The muskellunge swam back and forth below his hands several times, his great form plainly visible in the clear water.

"That fellow must weigh thirty-five pounds," said Dick, an experienced fisherman. "He's the fiercest game fish in these waters. I can hardly believe this."

Then came the climax of Olie's exhibition. The muskellunge reached its head out of the water and took the worms from Olie's fingers. Olie was cautious. He kept the offering at the tips of his fingers and dropped the worm as the big fish got near his hand. The muskellunge's teeth are sharp as saws, and he might have difficulty in

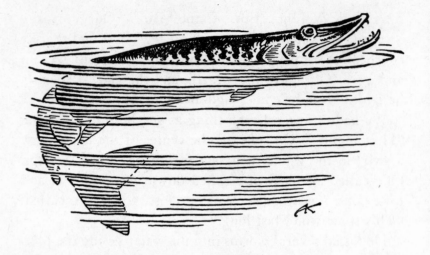

knowing where the worms left off and Olie's fingers began.

"Easy there, Jim," Olie was saying. "Don't get rambunctious. Ye got company today, so behave yerself. This is yor appetizer, now next comes yor dinner."

Olie took a package from his pocket in which were food scraps saved from his cupboard. The big fish swirled about, waiting. Then he whipped the surface of the water into waves and eddies as he gathered up every last crumb Olie tossed to him. The meal finished, Jim headed speedily for distant places. Near the middle of the lake he broke water as if in high glee. "Atta boy, Jim!" yelled Olie. "Go-'head show 'em what you can do." Then the tall old man drew himself up proudly and turned to us. "Believe it?" he asked.

"Olie, I wouldn't believe it if I saw anyone else do it," I said. "Of you and animals I would believe anything."

"Amazing!" Dorothy said. Sonya just walked up and took hold of Olie's hand.

"When I tell my friends that I saw a musky come when it was called," Dick said, "I expect they'll have people chasing me with butterfly nets."

"Jist don't tell where you saw it," Olie requested. "Some kind o' so-called sportsmen would like nothin' better 'n to catch Jim."

Grandmaw strutted by now and took Sonya's attention. Olie looked at Dorothy. "How you gettin' along now, lady?" he asked.

"Oh, fine," she replied, puzzled at his question.

"I don't mean yor health," Olie said. "I mean, how you doin' about animals? Are ye gettin' rid of yer fears?"

Dorothy flashed a look at him. "It isn't easy, Warden Olie," she said, "but I'm trying, and I believe I'm making progress."

"Good fer you!" he declared. "Nice thing is ye want to do somethin' about it. Ye know, lady," he said seriously, "ye don't love animals jist for Sonya, and not jist for the animals. It's mighty important fer yor own sake. That ol' human heart—" he touched his chest with his fingers— "warn't ever built fer fear or hate, ye know. Mighty bad fer us when we use it that way. It's all shaped and built fer love, and ye'll be a much happier woman if ye go-'head and love everything."

"I'll go-'head-in-there and do it," Dorothy affirmed.

"Go-'head-in-there good fer you!" Olie laughed.

"But tell me, Warden Olie—" there was almost des-

peration in Dorothy's voice—"did you always like animals? Didn't you have to learn to like them?"

Olie was startled at the question. He was silent for a
time, his eyes taking on a faraway look. Then his whiskers moved about, the outward evidence of a smile beneath.
"There's a story 'bout that," he said. "I'll tell it to you
sometime, if you want."

But we had to wait for that until our next visit.

XIV

FUN, SPILLS AND PORKY QUILLS

"Loony Coon, how *do* you manage to get cuter all the time?"

Loony Coon looked up at Giny as if he understood her question and loved its flattery. We were taking moving pictures, and as usual he was the star performer. The other members of the cast were back in the brush, and for the moment he had the stage to himself, a situation that suited his pride perfectly. He wore an expression that seemed to say, "Aw, it's easy when you know how. Have a look at this!" Taking a position in the very center of our woodland stage, he sat on his haunches, his fat little tummy spreading out shapelessly, his head turned at a saucy angle and his front paws hanging limply at his sides. He looked like some abbreviated edition of an Oriental idol.

Our applause and the grinding of the movie camera were just what he needed to goad him on to his next stunt. Slowly and deliberately but looking as if he were unmindful of what he was doing, he reached down with his front paws and took hold of his own hind foot. For a moment he kept feeling his toes, rolling them about between his front paws in that amusing way raccoons handle things.

"Do you suppose he knows that hind foot belongs to

125

him?" Giny asked. "That's just the way he does with a piece of bread, or a grain of corn. Now what is he going to do?"

If possible, Loony Coon was sillier than ever. His left ear drooped more, his right one stood up straighter, and his eyes looked up into the night as though he were looking at flying pink elephants. Then his front paws started pulling on his hind foot. When it didn't come easily, he pulled on it harder. The hind foot jerked back. Impatiently he grabbed it again and pulled. It tried to jerk away again, but he held on and pulled and pulled—until with one supreme effort he threw himself completely off balance and went rolling head over tail down a little hill.

"Loony Coon, I can't stand it!" Giny laughed, holding her hands to her sides.

But Loony Coon hadn't finished his act. He came back and searched all about, apparently looking for that hind leg or whatever it was that had tipped him over. Failing to find it, he assumed his idollike position once more. With the same silly look on his face he began groping beneath himself for that funny thing. I suppose he figured that's where it was before, and it ought to be there again. It was. While his eyes looked up at the treetops, his front feet took hold of one hind foot and tugged. The solo wrestling match was stirring but brief. The front feet won, and Loony Coon went rolling downhill again.

"Loony Coon, you're wonderful!" Giny cried when she could get sufficient breath.

"Sh-h-h-h," I cautioned as I readjusted my movie camera. "Don't praise him too much. If he ever finds out how valuable he is to my pictures, he'll demand a Hollywood salary. I couldn't afford to pay him what he's worth."

"Oh, he doesn't have fancy ideas," Giny assured me. "Raise his salary to half a pound of peanuts per night and I'll give him a bonus of some homemade cookies. He'll be content. You see, he has no income tax to pay, he grows his own fur coat, nature furnishes him a mansion with a swimming pool, and he doesn't need a costly car. Wait a minute—" Giny started toward the kitchen—"I have an idea."

She put a handful of peanuts in a milk bottle, then tied a string about the neck of the bottle and hung it on the limb of a tree. It dangled within reach of the raccoons. I switched on the full floodlights and stood expectantly with my camera.

At first nothing happened. Several contingents of raccoons were now arriving at Campbells' Cafeteria, and there were the usual feuds to be settled before they could give their attention to anything else. Big Boy came but he didn't stay long. Andrea and her whole family took out after him. They ran him right off the island. Dignified Lady was there with her three cubs. A new family came timidly out of the brush, a mother with four young. Giny identified Rackett, a raccoon we had known for years, and Clubby, the fast-moving male with one mutilated foot. He had been a visitor for several seasons, but we never really gained his friendship. Altogether there were sixteen customers this August evening.

Blondy was the last to put in an appearance—and what an appearance! Hobbling along on three legs and holding his stub leg up, he moved unhesitatingly and confidently right up to us.

"Such a fat raccoon!" I exclaimed. "Blondy, old top, you don't need any sympathy, do you?"

"Not a bit," said Giny, stroking him. "He has more fun on three legs than most coons do on four. Why, Blondy, you're getting to be as wide as you are long! Here, have a peanut." She offered him this much favored bit of food but he refused it. "What's the matter with you, fussy?" she said. "This is a peanut, you remember, your favorite."

Blondy took the peanut from her, laid it on the ground at his feet and looked up with a begging expression. I offered him a piece of bread but he still refused to eat. We gave him a pan of dog food. He sniffed at it but not a bite did he take.

"I know what he wants," Giny said. "I baked today, and he got wind of those cookies and the cake. Nothing doing, Blondy," she addressed the coon. "You're much too fat right now. We've spoiled you, that's what we've done. Eat this food—it's better for you. Here, any dog in America would like a chance at this dish." She pushed the pan toward the reluctant raccoon.

Blondy wasn't impressed by the knowledge of what

some dog would like. His kind isn't especially fond of dogs anyway. He pawed at the dish, caught it with his claws and turned it over, spilling it all over our steps. Then he sat down and looked at Giny.

"Don't look at me that way, Blondy," she begged. "I can't stand it."

Blondy knew she couldn't. He was putting on an act, and doing it well. He had done it before and would do it again—every time those good baking aromas came from Giny's kitchen. The longer she coaxed, the droopier he became. He looked more and more pathetic, while Giny cringed under the pressure of sympathy. At just the strategic moment he raised his stub leg and waved it slowly toward Giny. That did it! Giny fairly flew into the house and rushed back with a plateful of cookies and cake. "Take it, you brute!" she exclaimed as she placed it before the triumphant Blondy. "You know how to work me, don't you? I could skin you alive for it, but if you want any more cookies, just let me know."

If a raccoon can smile, Blondy did. Taking a big bite of fresh cooky, he looked up at me with something that resembled a wink. "You're pretty dumb, old top," I commented. "Dumb like a fox. I'm studying your methods. Maybe I'll try them and get some of those cookies myself."

"No, you don't," Giny warned. "I have to save them— for Blondy."

Our attention was now drawn to Loony Coon. He had discovered the milk bottle. It both fascinated and frightened him. The peanuts he recognized, but what was that thing they were in? He advanced cautiously toward the strange contraption. When within a few inches of it he lost his nerve and backed up. The bottle didn't talk back, so he moved toward it again. This time he touched it with his nose. Just at that instant Blondy stepped on the cooky plate and upset it with a loud clatter. Loony Coon almost jumped out of his hide, disappearing into the darkness!

It was some minutes before he could regroup himself for a fresh assault. This time the battlefield was quiet and he became more confident and bold. He wanted those peanuts the worst way. He bit the bottle, he scratched it, he growled at it, he wrestled with it, but still the peanuts remained undisturbed and the bottle hung complacently.

"Loony Coon," called Giny, "if you look at the top of that milk bottle, you'll find an opening. Maybe that will help you."

"And hurry up," I requested. "I'm running out of film."

Loony Coon didn't need any instructions or urging. His inquisitive front feet had already reached up and found the opening in the bottle. The trouble was the opening was above his head and he couldn't reach into it with his paw. Nudging the bottle with one foot, he pushed it far to one side, striving desperately to reach inside with the other foot. Presently it slipped from his grasp and swung on the string far away from him. His curiosity turned to fright when the thing changed its

course and started back at him. Unable to believe his
eyes, he watched it come on and on until it struck him
right on his floppy ear. He jumped, turned a flip and
vanished into the woods.

We didn't see him again for an hour. His sudden flight frightened all the other coons away too, all save Blondy, who was still too contented with his cake and cookies to get excited about anything.

Big Boy emerged from the woods now. He looked about the feeding area for his competitors. Finding himself in possession of the place, he walked calmly up to the milk bottle and surveyed the situation for a moment. Then he unhurriedly and deliberately chewed the string in two and let the bottle down onto the ground. Now he could reach into the bottle and get the peanuts with ease. He had them all eaten before Loony Coon came back.

One evening Andrea's circus was somewhat late in arriving. The other raccoons had come, but not our little family. Giny was on the lookout for them. Presently she called to me, much distress in her voice. "Sam, Sam, come quickly. Andrea's face is filled with porcupine quills!"

I went to Giny and she directed my attention out the window to the coons. It was as Giny had said. One side of Andrea's jaw had twenty or more quills in it, and there were others sticking in her nose.

"What can we do?" Giny asked. "The quills will just work deeper and deeper, won't they?"

"Yes, they will," I agreed, much disturbed. "I'm not sure what we can do. Perhaps I can catch her in a net and remove them." It was the only idea that came to me, but I knew it was not an easy solution. Friendly as Andrea was, she would fight such treatment. Once I saw four men take porcupine quills from a baby raccoon, and it required their combined efforts to hold the creature. The strength of these animals when they are under stress is amazing.

"I'll need help," I said. "Perhaps Ray will come, and Dick. You keep track of her till I return."

I hastened off by boat to the mainland and by car to get my friends. It took nearly an hour to round up the men and some strong net equipment. When we came back Giny met us, smiling.

"What's happened?" I asked. "Where's Andrea?"

"Come and see, all of you," said Giny, much happier than I had expected to find her.

At the edge of the brush we could see Andrea and with her was Loony Coon. To our utter amazement the cub was pulling out the porcupine quills! Already Andrea's nose was free and most of the quills were out of her jaw. She was licking the side of Loony Coon's head, while he continued his work.

"Wuzzling!" I exclaimed.

"Yes, wuzzling!" Giny agreed.

The next night when we saw Andrea there was not a quill left in her face.

XV

MISTAKEN IDENTITY

"Snow! And this is only the fifteenth of August," Giny mused as we stood looking out our cabin windows. The distant shore of our lake was hazy and almost obscure in a downpour that was driven by a hard north wind. In among the raindrops occasional flakes of snow were like advance scouts of winter blizzards.

"Autumn always comes early in this north country," I reminded her. "This kind of storm makes the cabin feel cozy and inviting, doesn't it?"

"I love it," Giny said warmly. "There are other signs of fall too. Did you notice a bright-red branch on our big maple tree?"

"Yes, and I've seen several deer in their heavy winter coats."

"The swallows left almost two weeks ago," she added. "I saw them lined up on our light wires."

"The good old north country!" I stared at the pines swaying in the strong wind. "It's severe, tough, but strong and sincere. Do you know whom it reminds me of?"

Giny looked up for my reply.

"Warden Olie," I said, and she nodded her agreement.

"He's rough and rugged, but he has great sincerity and like the forest a tender side to his nature. Who was it wrote, 'Pray not for easier tasks but for greater strength'?"

"I don't remember, but it's something Olie might have said," Giny replied. "Look—" she pointed outside another window where two chickadees were fluttering, trying to get our attention—"there's another advance sign of autumn. The birds are working hard at storing up food."

She brought them a handful of crumbs and the two birds eagerly snatched the morsels and flew away with them. So did six other chickadees who heard of the feast and two white-breasted nuthatches and four red-breasted nuthatches. This kept up until Giny's hand was thoroughly chilled and she withdrew it. Immediately the chickadees were fluttering at the window again. I took over the task of feeding them, while Giny warmed her hands at the fireplace.

"The raccoons' fur coats are getting heavier every day," she said, continuing our autumn observations.

"And the young ones are so large it's getting difficult to distinguish them from the adults," I added.

"Our woodchucks are so fat their stomachs drag on the ground," she went on. "They remain in their holes for several days at a time as though they were about to start hibernation. Do you suppose this could prophesy early winter?"

I shook my head. Animals seem to know no more about weather than we do. Squirrels and rabbits growing thick fur, beavers building their houses extra heavy, bears getting unusually fat, ducks flying south early—all these signs are supposed to predict a severe winter. And yet I have seen them all followed by mild seasons. Animals show lots of wisdom, but apparently long-range weather prediction is not a part of it.

"Oh, that reminds me: I saw another seasonal development," Giny said. "Andrea was quarreling with her babies and chasing them last night—even Loony Coon. I think she's starting to wean them—and I just dread it."

In the next several nights we saw clearly that this severe, almost cruel period was at hand. The young raccoons had to be taught to depend on their own abilities. Andrea and the other mothers had provided for them as far in life as was wise.

The wild-creature way of carrying out this weaning process was a bit distressing to see, especially for Sonya. The next evening when the Ecks called she saw the change taking place and she didn't like it.

There were tears in her eyes as she came back from feeding her pets. "Mother," she said to Dorothy . . . And then there were a few seconds in which no other words would come out. With a little effort she gained control of herself to continue. "She bit him. Andrea bit Loony Coon. She bit him hard and made him cry. She growled at him and chased him and . . ." The tears got the best of her again.

"She won't really hurt him, dear." Dorothy took her

in her arms. "Sam and Giny have been telling us about it. She's just telling him that he's a big raccoon now and that he can take care of himself."

"But does she have to be so mean about it?" The words came out between sobs.

"Andrea isn't mean, Sonya," I said. "She's talking to him the only way he'll understand."

"But . . . but . . . but they had so much fun together. Why couldn't they just go on that way?"

Sonya was hard to console. She had idealized the relationship of Loony Coon and Andrea. Even when I assured her that Loony Coon would not want to be a baby all his life, that he would want to be like other raccoons and make his own living and his own home in the forest, she was not convinced.

"But will they always be mean to one another?" she questioned. "Won't they ever be friends again."

"Yes, they'll be friends again, Sonya," Giny said. "Every year we've seen baby raccoons weaned and we always feel sad when it happens. But as soon as the mother has trained her babies to look out for themselves, then they run together again."

"How long will that take?"

"Probably in three or four weeks they'll be friendly again."

Sonya smiled just a little bit. Apparently there was a ray of hope in her cloud of gloom.

"Giny and I believe that during this period the father

raccoon takes over some of the cub training," I said to Dorothy and Dick. "So little is really known about animals, and observation of them is so difficult, we're not sure, but our experience with them suggests it. Often we've seen the weaned cubs running with the big males. We'll be watching Loony Coon now to see if we can learn something."

Sonya returned to her raccoons now. Among the animals it sounded as if a constant brawl was going on. Loony Coon approached Andrea again and again, as if he couldn't believe she really meant to treat him so mean. The other young ones of the family took the situation more philosophically. Yet Andrea never weakened. She gave Loony Coon a severe trimming every time he came near and sent him yelping into the brush.

"Andrea," we heard Sonya pleading with her, "do you have to be that way? Couldn't you train him a little bit each day and not all at once?"

Dorothy was about as much affected as Sonya. She stood at the door looking out. "I never felt so sorry for anything before in my life," she said. "Andrea, I could spank you—or I wish I could."

This seed of sympathy had taken root in Dorothy's heart. In days that followed it seemed to outgrow much of her antipathy to animals. Almost every night Loony Coon and his gang called at the Eck cabin after he left our place. Always she had something special for him. Remembering her earlier experience, she baked an apple pie for him—and made an extra one for Dick.

When we called on them one evening we found the Ecks in high spirits. Something had happened that made even Sonya forget her regret of the raccoon weaning. "Guess what happened?" Dorothy exclaimed excitedly. "No, don't guess. You'd never believe it possible. I—" she reached over her shoulder and patted herself on the back—"I, even I, have picked up Loony Coon! Now what do you think of that?"

"Wonderful!" cried Giny. "Tell us about it."

"Well, last night when they were here Andrea was extra mean to him. We heard such awful fighting we went out. She had Loony Coon pinned to the ground and she was chewing on him. He sounded like a whole cageful of monkeys. I didn't know I was going to do it, or I wouldn't have let myself, but I rushed out and frightened Andrea away. Then, believe it or not, I picked up Loony Coon. He was still crying from the way he'd been treated.

"He was so miserable," Dorothy went on, "and he needed cuddling. When I took him he just nestled in my arms. And then he reached up and put his arms or his paws or whatever he has—he put them around my neck and clung to me. Why, I even brought him in the house!"

"Yes, and fed him marshmallows," put in Sonya.

"And chocolate creams," Dick added.

"Well, he had something coming." Dorothy was emphatic. "You know, I feel as if I'm going to be as crazy about animals as you are, Sam. I can hardly wait for Loony Coon to come back tonight."

She didn't have to wait long. We continued our conversation until there was a rattling of the refuse can on the back porch.

"There he is now!" Dorothy exclaimed, rising and heading for the back door. "Wait, I'll show you what I can do. I'll bring Loony Coon right in, in my very own arms!"

She rushed out of the room and we heard the back door open. Then suddenly we heard her give an ear-splitting scream that sent Dick and me running to the back door. Dorothy passed us as we went, letting out one shriek after another. I snatched a flashlight from my pocket and sent a ray from it into the night. Far down the lane that leads from the house I caught sight of a large black bear, running so fast his hind legs almost passed his front legs.

Back in the living room Dorothy was in Giny's arms, nearly hysterical.

"There, there!" I said as we all gathered about her. "It was nothing but a bear. He wouldn't hurt you. You've frightened him out of the county."

"I've frightened him?" Dorothy cried. *"I've* frightened *him?* What do you think he has done to me? I never want to see an animal again. I don't even want a canary bird. Loony Coon can jump in the lake. I——"

"Mother, dear," said Sonya's soft voice, "why didn't you bring him in the house so I could see him? You know, I've never seen a wild bear."

Dorothy looked from one of us to another, utterly lacking words, until we all burst out laughing.

"Yes, that's what I should have done, Sonya," she said, making her way weakly to a chair. "I should have picked him up as I did Loony Coon and brought him in for you to see. He would only weigh about——"

"Four hundred pounds," I suggested.

XVI

LOONY COON TAKES THE CAKE

THE weaning of Loony Coon and his generation was carried out relentlessly. Raccoons don't bluff about this sharp and vital change in the family life. When baby days are over there is not a moment of maternal pity for the cubs, not a smidgen of sympathy to soften the shock.

But if the mother coons were severe in administering the discipline, Loony Coon and his pals were strong and self-reliant in taking it. In their characters live the solid qualities of the wild that ask no softness. For the first few hours only was there any whimpering on their part, when they saw the mother care slipping away from them. But once they realized this was a new phase of life opening up, they met it spontaneously.

Giny and I were busy these evenings making observations. It was baffling work. Being nocturnal animals, raccoons hide their habits and ways of living behind a cloak of darkness.

"It's like peeking through a knothole in a fence at a baseball game," Giny complained. "We see only enough to make us realize how much more there is to see."

"Well, what *have* we learned?" I questioned. "One

142

thing certain: the adult females are more sociable with one another now that the young are weaned."

"Yes," she agreed. "When the young were with them they fought one another. Now Andrea, Lady, Rackett and the other mothers are quite chummy. They come in together to feed. And the cubs are so much more friendly with the males now."

"Also with one another!" I added.

These were generalizations and not very satisfying. However, one evening we saw something definite through our "knothole," as Giny named our limited observations. We were canoeing close in to shore in our West Bay when Big Boy, the huge male raccoon, emerged from the brush close to us. He looked at us for a moment as if he didn't know what or who we were. I am convinced that raccoons are very nearsighted creatures.

"It's all right, Big Boy," called Giny. "Don't be afraid, pet; it's just Sam and I."

Even if Big Boy did not know us by sight, he did by sound. Immediately recognizing our voices, he abandoned all caution and went to work along the shore of this bay. Sphagnum moss grows on the surface of the water like a shelf. Big Boy felt about with a thoroughness that covered every inch of the territory. It wasn't long before he came up with a crawfish, which he ate with obvious relish.

"Big Boy," exclaimed Giny critically, "how indelicate! No cooking, no salt, no pepper—how can you eat things that way?"

Big Boy didn't hear. He was too busy with his hunting or fishing—whichever it might be called.

"Giny," I whispered excitedly, "look who's coming!"

"Loony Coon!" she cried. "You rascal, what are you doing there?"

Loony Coon had no time for greetings or for words. He was all business. Following the trail of Big Boy by

scent, he emerged from the brush, entered the water and took up the same activity as the larger raccoon. He caught a crawfish, and to Giny's horror he caught a bloodsucker too.

"Loony Coon," she cried, "I wouldn't have believed it of you! I wish I hadn't seen you do that."

Loony Coon went on working, casting a glance at Giny which seemed to say, Enough of that baby stuff. Don't you know I've been weaned? I'm a big he-man coon now.

The two creatures worked their way on down the shore line. This mission completed, they disappeared into the woods, Big Boy leading the way and Loony Coon following. Clearly Big Boy by his example was an important factor in Loony Coon's education.

Later the same evening these two came together to the feeding station on our island. Andrea was there, and Loony Coon ventured near her only once. She snarled and showed her teeth. That was all Loony wanted to know. He went back to Big Boy. Other cubs from the several families were working about the area, some in play with one another, some attached to older males.

"Sam," called Giny a few moments later, watching out the window, "here's something to see."

"What's happening?" I asked, coming up beside her.

"See, Big Boy is trying to open the front door and Loony Coon is watching."

It was nothing new to have Big Boy open our screen door. He had learned how in previous years. The door did not hook properly and he always took advantage of the fact. Inserting his left front foot into the crack and bracing his right paw against the jamb, he opened the door easily and held it while he looked about the room. This clever display brought a reward that he knew was coming—a bit of marshmallow, his favorite food. He backed away, letting the door slam.

"Look at Loony Coon!" exclaimed Giny. "He's fairly drooling for that marshmallow. Big Boy, give him a bite."

But generosity was not in Big Boy's make-up. While Loony Coon looked on he chewed the marshmallow, swallowed it and came back for more.

"Shall I give Loony Coon some?" Giny asked. "He looks so pathetic."

"Not just yet, please," I replied. "Let's watch a while. Here comes Big Boy again. I want to see how strong he pulls."

The strength of the big animal was amazing. I tried holding the screen door shut, but he pulled it right out of my hands. Giny gave him a second marshmallow, and he promptly ate it in front of the tantalized Loony Coon.

"I just have to give Loony one," Giny insisted, watching the young coon.

"Wait, please," I urged. "Here he comes. Let's see if he has learned from observation."

The young animal was sensing a connection between the screen-door opening and the tasty food. He walked up to the door and smelled at the crack. Then he sat down and felt about with his front feet. He rose high on his back feet and looked through the screen at us.

"You have to earn things in this life, Loony," I said in fatherly tones. "Do as Big Boy does and you'll get the same reward."

Loony Coon examined the crack again. While he hesitated, Big Boy literally swept him aside, pulled the door

open and got his third marshmallow. The door slammed,
Big Boy devoured his tidbit, and Loony Coon looked for-
lorn. Then he started pawing at the door. He pulled it
open a little, then lost his hold. Encouraged, he made
another try. Again it slipped. A third time he pulled at
it and open it came!

"Eureka, Loony Coon!" cried Giny. "You've found the
way. Here's your reward for persistence and industry."

She held out a marshmallow toward him and he reached
for it. Right there he discovered he had not yet learned
all Big Boy knew about this business. Doors of this sort
won't stay open of their own accord. He reached for the
marshmallow, let go the door, and it promptly slammed
on his tail! There was a wild flurry as he whirled about
to do battle with whatever had bitten him. He butted the
door open and raced into the yard. When he recovered
from his fright a few minutes later he tried it all again
and this time held the door until he could retreat with a
marshmallow in his mouth. From then on Loony Coon
knew how to open a door—a dangerous bit of learning
for one of his mischievous disposition. We found that
out.

The yellow moon of August was full. The weather had
mellowed and the evenings were inviting. Mosquitoes,
which diminish somewhat every outdoor pleasure of the
north country, were fewer.

"It's a wonderful time for campfire dinners," Giny declared one day. "We should be having some, for the season is slipping away."

"Indeed we should," I agreed. "Let's have one tonight."

The Ecks came and so did Ray and Ada. Sonya had a new camera her father had got for her while he was on a business trip to the city. It was equipped with flashlight attachment, and she had plans for photographing everything in the north. While the campfire dinner was being cooked and the table being set, she worked around like a veteran newspaper cameraman. She made mistakes, of course—who doesn't with a camera? But Sonya was eager to learn, and each error finally was corrected with increased knowledge.

The sun set just as dinner was ready. It was a tempting repast, and our appetites were typical of outdoor life. The moon, looking huge and made of gold, crept up from the eastern horizon. It laid a yellow trail through the lake.

"Wonderful decorations we have for our dining room!" Ada commented as she helped arrange food on the table. "That sunset and that moonrise—how do you ever manage such things?"

"We have the place decorated anew every day," I replied. "A little extravagant, to be sure, but we have a charge account with nature."

"And we have a surprise for you," Dorothy broke in, taking a cover off a large pan they had brought along.

"Look! An angel-food cake. Sonya made it herself!"

It was a beautiful cake with white frosting and we lavished praise on Sonya.

"This is the first time in our experience that we have had angel-food cake at a campfire dinner." I laughed. "What would Daniel Boone think of this?"

"He'd want some of it, I'm sure," Giny said. "It's wonderful, Sonya. Thank you."

Sonya blushed and smiled sweetly. "Really, Mother made it—I just helped. Looks as if we should have made more," she went on, pointing into the brush. "We have company."

Here came Loony Coon and Big Boy, apparently following the scent of that cake.

"No, you don't!" I cried, taking the cake from Dorothy. "This is angel food and that makes it none of your business." The two raccoons stood on their hind legs and reached high. There was no question about what they sought. "Nothing doing," I affirmed. "Cake isn't good for little raccoons. You go and eat a nice bloodsuck-er——"

"Br-r-r-r-r." Giny shivered.

"Go to the cabin," I argued with the coons, who still reached up, clawing at my breeches and trying to get the cake. "There is some nice dog food. It has vitamins and all that sort of thing."

"Couldn't they have just a little bite?" Sonya teased. "Maybe just a taste would be all they want."

"No. Raccoons and angel-food cake don't belong together." I still held the cake high.

Big Boy and Loony Coon were not easily discouraged. They kept on arguing their right to that cake until Sonya brought them each one of their loved marshmallows. Then they went toward the house and we thought we were rid of them. I placed the precious cake on a service table near the fire until desserttime arrived.

While we were eating dinner our attention was drawn to a large, beautiful buck who appeared at the nearest point of the mainland. He was difficult to see in the soft, mingled light of moonbeams and afterglow, but we could make out his form and see his fine antlers. After drinking several times he waded into the water. To our surprise, he began swimming directly toward the island. We kept as quiet as we could, and it looked as if he meant to land at our very campsite. His swimming was swift and strong. The water fairly foamed about his shoulders and neck. We were entranced at the sight. Each member of our party whispered exclamations of admiration.

Then the fire changed the course of events. Suddenly it gave forth a loud *pop*. Startled, the buck altered his plan and swam off at increased speed. We watched him until he landed on a far shore and then heard him running into the brush.

"Wasn't he beautiful?" Ada gasped.

"I can never forget it—the sheer beauty of it," Dorothy added. "The moonlight, the woods, the smooth waters, the afterglow—and that deer swimming."

"All this and angel food too?" I paraphrased a line of poetry.

"That's what you think," Dick said excitedly. "Do you see what I see?"

We looked around and there was Loony Coon up on the service table, reaching his front feet toward the cake. Everyone shouted at once and everyone tried to get up at once. There was wild confusion as we stumbled all over one another. I gave a war whoop that went echoing about

the shores. Loony Coon was only speeded by the racket we made. Realizing that he was discovered and that he had only a split second to complete his mission, he lunged toward the cake.

"Loony Coon, don't you dare!" Giny screamed.

But Loony Coon dared. Escaping my grasp by inches, he lifted the whole cake into his mouth, jumped from the table and raced back into the brush, followed by Big Boy.

We stood looking at one another dumfounded. It was Sonya who first found her voice. She gave a delighted little giggle. "Goody! I really baked it for him."

XVII

ENCORE

"IT SEEMS to me we have a good excuse for another campfire party very soon," Giny said. We were saying good night after Loony Coon's pilfering episode.

"Right!" I agreed. "We have an angel-food cake due us. Sonya, would you bake another?"

Sonya was enthusiastic. A campfire party was her idea of the most fun one could ever find.

"Let's have it tomorrow night," Dorothy suggested. "The moon will still be full—and maybe Loony Coon will be too. Then he would let our cake alone."

"I'll fix him," I promised confidently. "If he tries that stunt again I'll pull his tail feathers out."

"He doesn't have tail feathers," Sonya corrected.

"Well, I'll pull them out anyway."

So it was that the very next night we assembled about our campfire once more. All day long Sonya had been whipping, stirring, mixing and splashing ingredients about their kitchen. Dorothy said the place looked as if plasterers had just finished a sloppy job. Anyhow, the result was a very fine-appearing angel-food cake, and Sonya showed justifiable pride as she presented it to me.

"Wonderful!" I exclaimed, holding it out for everyone to see. "No little bum of a raccoon is going to get

153

this cake. We'll put it in the cabin for safekeeping until the time comes to eat it."

I took the delicacy into the cabin and placed it in the kitchen. Then I returned to the group where all were working at dinner preparations in a most merry mood.

The very evening air seemed charged with happiness. The sun had dipped below the western horizon and Venus, the evening star, peered through the afterglow. In the east the moon rose in glory, laying its golden path through the waters.

Ray started a familiar song and soon the whole group joined in. Dick sings bass well and Dorothy a fine alto, so there was harmony. If occasionally there was a sour chord, it could be overlooked in the mood of the moment. I walked down to the lake shore and along the water's edge so I could get the effect of this singing from a distance. I sat on a log, my heart full of the blessing of this experience. Loony Coon and Big Boy came up to me. I had peanuts for them in my pocket and they knew it.

"You young scoundrel!" I said to Loony Coon as I fed him and stroked his head. "I ought to be mad at you after what you did. Now tonight behave yourself, do you understand? And that goes for you too, Big Boy."

The two of them cracked peanuts while I scratched back of their ears. Loony Coon climbed into my lap. He reached up with his little cold nose and touched mine. Then he began feeling about my face with his front feet. My nose, my eyes, my ears were all thoroughly investigated.

"This soft stuff is all right if you're saying you're sorry about last night," I said to him. "But if you're trying to cut yourself in on the cake again, you might as well stop. Not a crumb do you get! Understand?"

Loony Coon put both paws about my neck in a sort of hug, and I wondered if I wanted the cake after all. That moment I heard Sonya calling my name. Dinner was ready. So I went back, the two raccoons following.

Loony Coon drew a volley of uncomplimentary boos as he walked into the circle. Sonya took his picture. He ignored it all, walked over to the table where the cake had been the night before and stood on his hind legs.

"Did you ever get fooled!" Ray taunted. "Thought you'd find another cake, didn't you? Well, you're out of luck, Loony Coon, just out of luck."

Loony Coon walked away disappointed, Sonya following him with an offer of peanuts. He refused them.

"He wants cake, the old aristocrat," Giny said. "Not satisfied with ordinary food any more, now that he had a taste of Sonya's angel food. Loony Coon," she addressed him severely, "it isn't good for little coons to have so much sweet. Scat! Get out now! Go chew on some grass."

Loony Coon didn't scat. He and Big Boy sat looking the situation over, probably talking to each other in their silent language.

Our own dinner was interrupted halfway through by the arrival of an unexpected and unusual guest. A flying squirrel came coasting through the air and landed low on the trunk of a red pine tree near the fire. We could see him plainly in the firelight.

Sonya was delighted. "A flying squirrel?" she cried. "Oh, I never saw one before! Does he really fly?"

"No, Sonya," I answered. "A flying squirrel glides, but he doesn't fly like a bird. His front legs and back legs are attached by fur-covered skin. As he's going through the air he spreads his legs, and this skin acts like a parachute. He can glide long distances—sometimes a hundred feet or more."

"Fly! Fly!" she called to him. "Oh, how does he do it?"

The flying squirrel answered her question by demonstration. He skipped lightly up the tree to a point about forty feet from the ground and perched on a limb for a moment, looking around with his large protruding eyes. Then without hesitation he plunged out into the air. His legs spread and he glided gracefully down right over our heads. At the end of his flight he landed softly on a balsam tree, ran up to the first limb and there took a bow. We clapped our hands.

"How pretty!" exclaimed the excited Sonya. "Could I get his picture?"

She moved too fast for success. The squirrel wouldn't stand for her enthusiastic rush toward him. Before Sonya had half covered the distance to his tree he disappeared into the darkening woods, racing from one limb to another over aerial trails only squirrels can know.

"Sh-h-h-h," Dorothy quieted us. "Did you hear something—something like a door slamming?"

None of us had, in the excitement caused by the flying squirrel. We listened carefully. For a moment nothing was audible but the distant call of the whippoorwill. Then from the cabin came a sudden loud clatter and clash.

"What in the world could that be?" Giny asked. Then her eyes lighted with realization. "Sam," she exclaimed, rising, "Loony Coon—he can open a door! Quick, that cake!"

I needed no urging but was already on my way toward the cabin, flashlight in hand. I was too late. Just as I approached the door flew open, pushed violently out from within. There went Loony Coon racing into the woods with a delicious and costly angel-food cake in his mouth.

"No, you don't," I yelled, making a frantic dive for the animal.

"Yes, I do," grunted Loony Coon in his own language, easily avoiding me and heading with his prize for some secret spot where he could eat undisturbed.

Silence was the first reaction of our group as we just stood staring at one another. Then we broke out in laughter that went echoing about the lake.

"I wonder if he likes orange flavor just as well," Sonya said with her little giggle. "We didn't have any vanilla this time."

XVIII

LOONY COON, THE SOCIALITE

WE held an indignation meeting. Our resolve ran high that Loony Coon was not going to defeat us utterly.

"We will have a *third* campfire party tomorrow night!" Dorothy declared.

"And I will make a *third* angel-food cake," Sonya volunteered.

"Then may I suggest we eat it as an appetizer and get it all down before that thieving Loony Coon can find it!" This was Giny's idea, and we all agreed.

But Mother Nature thought the angel-food cake episode had gone far enough. That night she moved in a dull-gray cloud that covered the sky from horizon to horizon. The next day a cold, drenching rain drove across the north country, banishing from our thoughts all plans for campfire dinners.

For three days the storm continued in varying severity. Trees swayed in fitful winds and the forest dripped. I stretched a canvas over a ridgepole to make a shelter for the raccoons' food. There was no need to worry about the animals themselves. Their thick fur coats are equal to shedding water as well as cold. But their food pans flooded continually and needed protection.

One evening when the storm was at its worst Giny and

I sat before the fireplace in a dreamy mood. The books we had been reading rested in our laps, and we listened to the melodious drone of the rain on the cabin roof. Giny had left our inner door slightly ajar to admit the forest air.

Suddenly we heard the screen door open and the inner door swung wide. "Well, good evening!" Giny exclaimed. "Sam, we have a guest. Won't you come in?"

There stood Loony Coon, wet as a sponge! Looking up as much as to say, "Thank you, I already have," he walked slowly across the room. Ignoring our further greetings, he went to the bookshelf and stood looking over the books as if searching for a certain title. He reached up with his front feet and pawed at the dictionary until it fell to the floor at his feet. Then he began turning the pages.

"If you're looking for peanuts, you'll find that under the P's," Giny suggested.

"And angel-food cake is under the A's—or is it?" I added.

Loony Coon was not open to suggestions. Not satisfied with the dictionary, he pulled two other books down, then left them on the floor and walked over to us. He accepted a few bites of graham cracker in lieu of his favorite pastry but did so without much enthusiasm. Apparently it was not food he wanted. I tried him on peanuts, but he showed no interest.

"Is this just a social call?" Giny asked. "Loony Coon, you might have left your overshoes and raincoat at the door."

"Yes, and just entered in your bones," I suggested.

Loony ambled out into the kitchen, stood up and sniffed where the cake once sat just to make sure he wasn't missing anything. Then he returned and came close to the fire, dripping water all the way. He settled down between our chairs with an air of contentment as though he meant to stay.

There was another sound at the screen door now. We looked around to see Big Boy holding it open and looking in.

"Come on in, Big Boy," I called. "We were just about to discuss the world situation and the future of bloodsuckers and crawfish. Won't you join us?"

By his attitude Big Boy refused. Holding the door with his powerful foot, he looked at Loony Coon as though saying, "So this is where you are. I go walking my paws off searching for you everywhere and you sit there beside a fire. Come out in the woods where a raccoon belongs."

But Loony Coon never budged. He gave Big Boy one patronizing look and then turned his attention back to the fire. Big Boy accepted some graham crackers from us, then backed out into the rainy night and disappeared.

It was the beginning of a new intimacy with Loony Coon. "He actually likes to be petted," said Giny, reaching down and scratching his head. "We haven't had many coons who would permit that."

Loony Coon stayed with us for over an hour. He approved of the fire and apparently our companionship too. Presently we developed a little game. He looked so comfortable I just had to tease him. I reached down and poked his nose with my finger. With a sort of silly look on his face he raised one foot and struck at my hand after the manner of a kitten. I poked him again and he responded the same way.

"Don't disturb him!" Giny begged. "He looks so contented. Now let him alone."

I was obedient for a moment, but when Giny became absorbed in her book I poked his nose with my finger again. Up came that foot. Giny remonstrated with me and sympathetically stroked Loony Coon's head. "Is he teasing you, Loony?" she asked. "If he doesn't behave himself, we'll put him out in the rain and you and I will enjoy this fire by ourselves."

Teasing was such fun I just couldn't resist. When Giny looked away I raised my finger and pointed it at Loony Coon. He made that funny gesture with his foot, though I wasn't even near him. I did it again. So did he. From that time on every time I pointed my finger at the young coon, he waved that paw in a circle. He kept us in constant laughter. Presently he rose and walked slowly to the door, opened it and went out into the rainy night.

"See?" Giny scolded, "you teased him until he left. Aren't you ashamed?"

I went to the door and threw on the floodlight. There stood Loony Coon in the midst of a puddle, rain pelting down on him, looking this way and that as if he didn't know which way to go. "Loony Coon," I called.

He looked around. "Look, Loony Coon," I said, pointing my finger at him. He was fully twenty feet away, but up came his paw swinging in a circle. It was a farewell gesture. He disappeared into the brush, perhaps in search of Big Boy.

We learned that he went to the Eck cabin later that ,same night. They too were enjoying a cabin evening. They had popped corn and were sitting before a lively grate fire. Dorothy was reading aloud from a favorite book. The screen door opened and in came Loony Coon as wet as if he had been swimming. Sonya was most delighted. She asked him to come in and sit down, and he did—right in front of the fire. He was the center of attention for an hour. Popped corn was offered him and he ate a few kernels.

"Just a neighborly call," said Dick in telling of the experience. "He left quietly just as he came. When he got to the door to go out Sonya reached out her hand and said, 'Aren't you going to say good-by?' Then he did the funniest thing. He raised his paw and waved it in a circle, as if he were saying, 'So long.' Then out he went."

Loony Coon made regular social calls at both cabins after that and never did he forget the cunning gesture with his paw.

XIX

WATERMELON RIOT

THE rainy spell hung on to the point of monotony. Then one morning the wind swung to the north. The rain stopped. The solid gray sky broke into small islands of clouds that raced before the wind. Patches of blue sky grew larger and the sun peered through the openings. Raindrops still clung to the tips of pine needles, sparkling like jewels when touched by shafts of sunlight. The forest shook showers of moisture from its foliage and then hung itself out to dry.

We went to town for supplies. It wasn't that we were out of food, but the raccoons were. Our grocery bill for animals always is greater than it is for ourselves.

"Look at our list," Giny said as we began our shopping. "We want carrots and cabbage for the woodchucks, suet and seeds for the birds, cracked corn, dog food and peanuts for the raccoons and squirrels."

"At the bottom of the list isn't there at least a head of lettuce for us?" I asked. "We really ought to have something."

"I'll put it down," she answered. "The woodchucks like lettuce anyway."

Among other things we found in the market that day were watermelons. I bought four of them.

"Now what in the world are you going to do with four watermelons?" Giny asked. "They're huge and we couldn't eat even one."

"Holiday for raccoons," I replied. "If I remember rightly raccoons used to raid our watermelon patches down in Illinois. I want to see what Loony Coon and his gang will do with them. I've a notion this will be the making of some funny pictures."

It was late in the evening when we paddled over to our island, the canoe loaded with supplies. A perfect calm ruled the night, as though nature had wearied herself with her storms and now was content to be at rest.

"I hear something in our boathouse," Giny whispered.

"So do I. The flashlight is by your feet. Let's see what's going on."

She directed the long beam through the darkness to a place in the black outline of our island where our boathouse stood. There we beheld a strange and appealing sight. Our pier was lined with raccoons in single file, all looking out toward us, their eyes shining like coals in the rays of our light.

"Hello, coon-coons," called Giny, using her endearing term for them. "Is your dinner late? I'm sorry. We're coming as fast as we can. Look!" she said to me. "Loony Coon is the first one—see his flappy ear?"

"And Big Boy is right next to him," I added. "What a reception committee!"

Giny shut off the light so she might aid with the paddling, and we hastened toward our waiting friends. As

we drew near we could hear their little anxious calls. Giny turned the light on them again.

"Look at Loony Coon!" I exclaimed. "He's making that funny gesture with his front foot."

The sound of our voices apparently had awakened Loony Coon's memory of this little stunt. He raised his left front foot and swung it in a circle.

"That's his way of saying 'Hi,'" Giny said. It certainly looked like the signal many people use with that intimate form of greeting.

"You'd better have some peanuts ready," I suggested. "We're going to get mobbed as soon as they can reach us."

Mobbed was the right word. As the canoe glided in alongside of the pier, raccoons swarmed over us. We dealt out peanuts as fast as we could, but we didn't keep up with the demand. The silence of the night was broken with the cracking and chewing of peanuts by a dozen hungry coons.

"All right, fellers," I said, stepping out of the canoe onto the pier. "That's all for now. Everybody up to the house!" I clapped my hands and at the sound the animals raced away. While Giny and I followed the winding trail from our boathouse to the cabin, the coons took a short cut. When we arrived they were already lined up at the front door and the feast went on. I brought up the watermelons. "This is dessert for tonight," I said as I cut a large one in two. "Now let's see what happens."

Taking the two melon halves in my arms, I walked out among the raccoons. I never should have done that. When the scent of this new food drifted down to them they left their other food and made a dash for me. Really they stopped me right in my tracks. Their strong front feet caught hold of my boots and my breeches as each one tried to pull me in a different direction. I endeavored to hold the melon out of their reach, but they climbed right up my legs toward my shoulders.

"Help! Help!" I called to Giny. "I'm the center of a riot."

She looked out at my dilemma, but the only help I got was laughter and a lot of advice. "Be careful not to hurt them," she warned. "You wanted a funny picture. Well, you have it—or rather you're it. Why don't you put the melons down?"

"I will if they'll wait until I get to their feeding station," I replied. Moving forward laboriously, dragging a mass of raccoons on each leg, I managed to walk a few steps to the feeding area and there put the melon on the ground. Each half immediately became a milling, squabbling puddle of raccoons.

"Are you watching this?" I asked Giny.

"I surely am," she called back from the doorway. "I've never seen a watermelon so brutally treated before. Look at Loony Coon."

Our special pet had turned savage. He was squeezed away from the melon by the sheer weight of numbers. His several attempts to get back into the feast were met by a solid wall of raccoon flesh. In desperation he climbed right on top of the seething mass and worked his way headfirst down into the middle. In a moment he emerged with a mouthful of juicy, red watermelon, and he sat on his companions while he ate it.

Big Boy was getting pushed around too. He used a technique different from Loony Coon's. At first he tried to muscle in beside Andrea, who was having a wonderful time. She took a bite at him and he left. He tried two other approaches and got nipped each time. He sat down a few feet away as if discouraged.

"Poor Big Boy!" exclaimed Giny. "He's so big he could whip any of them, and yet he lets them abuse him."

"I have a notion to get him a half melon all his own," I said, starting for the house. "Remember, 'the meek shall inherit the earth.' "

"Wait a minute," Giny stopped me. "Maybe he's not so meek after all. Watch what he's doing."

Big Boy had only been planning his strategy. He arose now, turned his tail toward one of the raccoon groups and started backing up. As he came in contact with his greedy comrades, two of them snarled and bit at him. Apparently he had some dislike of being nipped in the face, but at the other end it made no difference to him. He kept right on backing up. Inch by inch he forced his way into the pool of coons, his huge size enabling him to push the others away. Right over the melon his back-up journey carried him, in spite of all opposition. Then he sprawled out, covering the melon with his big body, allowing only a few inches at one end where he could do his own eating.

The other raccoons lacked a sense of humor about it, however. They stood back for a moment studying what to do next. We expected a concerted attack on Big Boy, but it did not come. Instead there was a mild trend to the whole procedure. One by one the baffled coons came up to Big Boy and reached under him, bringing out bites of melon. He seemed to have no objection to this, just so long as he remained master of the situation.

The maudlin melon melee carried on into the night. In the morning when we looked out at the feeding station there wasn't a smidgen of the melon left, not even the green rind!

Fun like that has to be repeated. It has to be shared with others too, if one is to get the most out of it. So it was that on the following evening we had our friends Ray

and Ada and the Ecks to see the second performance of
the melon comedy.

Sonya brought her new camera with flashlight attachment. I set up my movie outfit and we were ready for the
show to begin. The raccoons were arriving one at a time.
"We'll hold the melon until a large number gets here,"
I said. "It will make a worse scramble and therefore a
better picture."

"I have a suggestion," Giny volunteered. "Why not
try a whole melon on them? I wonder what they would
do with it."

This proved an inspiration. When Loony Coon, Big
Boy, Andrea, Lady, Blondy and a dozen of the cubs had
put in an appearance, I carried a huge melon out and
placed it on the ground. They did not gang up on me as
on the night before, though I am sure this was because
the smell of the whole melon wasn't so strong as the
halves'. The big green object did not impress them as
being food at first. They regarded it with curiosity and
a degree of fear. Half a dozen of them circled it, pointing sniffing noses toward it but staying three feet or more
away.

"Go get it, Loony Coon!" Sonya urged. "Go get it!"

Loony was closest to the melon, his feet acting as if
they wanted to run while he wanted to stay. Nothing in
his experience had prepared him for this thing which lay
so silent and forbidding in front of him. Was it some kind
of turtle all bundled up in a shell, waiting to shoot its
head out and snap him if he got too close? Or was it a

puffed-up frog that would jump on a fellow at any moment? Maybe it was a peanut with the big head, or an acorn all swollen from the rain.

"He's going up to it," Sonya whispered excitedly.

"But he wishes he wouldn't," Dorothy commented. "Look how cautious he is. His nose is twitching, his hair is standing up on his back and his feet are trembling. If that melon would bark or growl, I think he'd jump right out of his hide."

Loony Coon had walked as close to the melon as he wanted to be. Now he was stretching out with his nose, sniffing frantically. I didn't want to be mean, but someway I couldn't help it. Just as he was about to touch the melon, I scraped my fingernail up the screen of the door. It made a sudden and sharp *zip,* startling in the silence of the moment.

"Ee-e-e-e-e-ek!" screamed Dorothy, taken by surprise.

"Sq-u-e-e-k!" went Loony Coon, turning a backward flip.

S-w-i-s-h went the whole mess of raccoons in one wild dash back into the woods.

Sonya shot a flash bulb aimlessly into the night.

"Sam!" Giny said sharply. "Why did you have to do that?"

"My finger just sort of slipped," I explained lamely. "I'm sorry." But the smile on my face belied my words.

"You are not," Giny remonstrated. "I could just annihilate you. Now our raccoons are probably over in the next county."

But they had not gone far and were soon back, looking with renewed curiosity and concern at the big green problem that stood so still and mysterious on the forest floor.

Now they tried more of the mob type of action. Loony Coon, Big Boy and Blondy advanced on the melon at the same time. After a few nervous little feints they moved boldly to the attack. My finger scraped a little at the screen, but Giny caught and held it.

"Behave yourself!" she whispered. "They're having trouble enough."

They were. Big Boy spread his strong feet about the melon as if he were striving to hug it into submission. Blondy tried to bite it, but his jaws could not open wide enough. Loony Coon got a silly look on his face and reached away underneath the melon, looking for some solution there. All was futile. The great green monster stoically repelled their efforts. From a few feet back a ring of spectator raccoons watched the proceedings.

Big Boy was becoming desperate. He growled at the watermelon and showed a fit of real temper. He gave the melon one powerful twist and started it rolling. This movement by the green monster was more than Loony Coon and the others could stand, and there was a sudden and complete exodus. The whole raccoon population vanished as quickly as though they had been erased from existence. We could hear them racing through the brush to the far margins of the island, while the melon went weaving its way down the slope until it splashed in the lake.

"Oh, Sonya, how funny!" Dorothy laughed. "Did you get the picture?"

"Oh-h-h-h-h," gasped Sonya, looking down at the camera she held in her hand. "I guess I forgot."

"You aren't the first photographer to do that, Sonya," I said, recalling some of my own foolish mistakes at camera hunting. "Get ready for more action. We'll get the melon, and the coons will be back."

The raccoons were in no hurry. Apparently that strange new creature had given them a scare that lasted awhile. We retrieved the melon from the water and placed it again in the feeding area, but no coon came near it for a long time.

The hour was late for Sonya and she crept into her father's lap and went to sleep. We were about convinced that our animals were not returning that night. Our guests were talking of going home when Ray looked out to the feeding station and announced, "Loony Coon's here!"

"Loony Coon," cried Sonya, sitting up and rubbing her eyes.

"Yes, Loony Coon—he's back at the melon."

We took our stations at the door and windows again to see what would happen next.

"Why, he's getting bites of melon!" Giny exclaimed. "See, he reaches underneath and brings out small pieces."

"So he is," I agreed. "How do you suppose he's getting inside?"

Big Boy was puzzled too. He came out of the brush

and looked inquiringly at Loony Coon, who was certainly making the most of his opportunity. One handful or footful of delicious red melon was crowded into Loony's eager mouth. When Big Boy got too close there were a snarl and a snap that told him all friendship was off for the time being. They got in a tussle that ended in a chase through the woods.

"What's that?" asked Sonya, pointing to the melon.

"A mouse! E-e-e-e-ek!" Dorothy cried.

It was a small deer mouse and he darted into the shadow under the melon. My curiosity was stirred and I went out to see what was going on. I rolled the melon over, and on its underside I found a small, round hole—undoubtedly the carving of the mouse. In fact, he was inside the melon and made a hasty exit before my eyes and right close to them too.

"Run!" Dorothy cried. "Climb a tree! Do something! It's a mouse."

"And a cute one," I replied. "Could you see his big ears?"

"Cute?" Dorothy moaned. "Oh, don't tell me I must learn to like mice too!" and she added a little *e-e-e-e-ek*.

"He was nice, Mother," Sonya insisted. "And see? He showed Loony Coon how to get into the melon."

Loony Coon was back. I pointed my finger at him and he responded with his "Hi" sign, so I yielded possession of the watermelon. That hole was all he needed. Every minute the hole got larger and the watermelon got hollower. Other coons gathered around, but Loony Coon considered possession as all ten points of the law and he had the hole. Greedily he scratched and clawed at the melon, swallowing down great chunks until the opening was as large as his head.

"Look, Mother," Sonya cried a few minutes later. "Look he has his whole head inside."

"I am looking, dear," said Dorothy, as excited as her daughter. "I can hardly believe what I see. Why, he's going farther in!"

Loony Coon worked furiously. This business of having his head in the melon had some advantages and some disadvantages. By monopolizing the opening he kept the other coons from edging in on the feast, but breathing in there was difficult and occasionally he had to come out for air. When he did a dozen raccoon paws would reach for the opening and snatch bites. Then in Loony would go again. Under the furious attack the melon was suffering considerable wear. Soon Loony got not only his head in but his front shoulders and feet as well.

"What *does* he look like?" Giny laughed. "Is it the dodo, the flightless bird?"

"Or a two-legged watermelon," Dick suggested. "Something never seen before on this earth," he concluded.

In sympathy with the other animals, I slipped out and cut another small hole in the melon. Blondy took over this opening, thrusting his good foot in and bringing out one bite after another. He was reaching farther and farther into the interior of the melon when suddenly he jerked his paw out and gave a little cry—the raccoon equivalent of "ouch!" Loony Coon, inside the melon, had bitten him!

Time passed unnoticed as we watched this woodland vaudeville. We ran out of laughs.

"I can't find another giggle," said Dorothy, looking at her wrist watch. "Why, Sonya Eck, do you know it's nearly three o'clock in the morning and you're still up? We must get you home."

"Oh, may I watch just a little while longer?" Sonya begged, wide awake with excitement. "I never saw anything like this before. See Loony Coon—I believe he has enough at last."

Loony brought his head out and he was a sorry-looking sight.

"People often joke about getting melon back of their ears," Dick said with a chuckle he had found somewhere. "He really has done it."

"Not only in his ears. In his whiskers, his eyes, under his chin—why, it's all over him," Giny added. "What a mess!"

Loony was smeared from head to foot and back again. He was so full he was shaped like the watermelon itself. He walked away unsteadily as if having difficulty carrying the load. Other coons made a dash for the melon, but he didn't care. The thing was about as hollow as a football, anyway. Sitting down and leaning back against a stump, he began the discouraging job of cleaning himself up. It was entirely too difficult, and so he simply rolled over on his side and went to sleep.

We bade one another good morning as the guests departed.

"You had better sleep all day tomorrow, Sonya," I suggested.

"I'll be glad to," she said sleepily; "that is, if I can dream about Loony Coon."

XX

A SKUNK'S GRATITUDE

WE heard that a large heron rookery had been discovered only a few miles from our Sanctuary. These tall, stilted birds are becoming scarce, and we were pleased to hear of the colony. Our information was that there were over a hundred nests and that the birds were very active.

"Sonya should see that," Giny said. "She has probably never seen a heron rookery. Let's stop by the Eck cabin and ask if they'd like to go with us."

We packed a lunch and drove to our friends' cabin. They were much interested in our herons but very busy. "We've budgeted this day to letter writing," Dorothy said. "Due mostly to that Loony Coon, both Dick and I have neglected our correspondence terribly. We'd better stay home and clear up some of this work."

"Could we borrow Sonya then?" Giny asked. "It's an easy trip?"

"Why, Sonya would love to go, wouldn't you, dear?" Dorothy looked down at the beaming youngster. "You're nice to want her."

Sonya was delighted. She coaxed her parents to come along, but they held to their plans.

"There's a little pride in the letters I'm writing," Dorothy said with a smug smile. "I'm telling my friends of my progress as an animal lover. Maybe I exaggerate just a bit, but I want them to be impressed."

"You do feel more comfortable with them, don't you?" I asked.

"Definitely. Last night I had Loony Coon in my lap and it gave me only two shivers. I expected it to give me a dozen."

"In other words, progress has been made but there's more work to do." Dick laughed. "Really, you're doing wonderfully, dear, and it's been a big job."

Dorothy took a deep breath but did not reply. She went about preparing Sonya for her journey to the herons' nests.

It was arranged that Sonya should remain with us until after dinner. In the evening Dorothy and Dick would call for her at the island by boat.

The heron rookery was not difficult to find. We followed a forest road for a few miles, then left our car and walked down a faint trail. Long before we reached the rookery we could hear the wild, unmusical cries of the birds. Sonya's eyes danced with excitement. "Oh, it's wonderful!" she cried. "I feel as if I were in the middle of the jungle."

"All right." Giny laughed. "Let's forget our car is back there half a mile and pretend we're buried in a wilderness."

Sonya liked that and she was good at pretending.

Some of the herons circled over us. Their flight was

graceful, their large wings flapping slowly and their long legs held straight and rigid behind them.

As we neared the rookery sudden silence fell on the bird population. "We've been discovered," I told Sonya. "Now the birds won't make a sound or a motion until they figure out what we are and what we mean to do. You'll have to look closely to see them, for they make themselves resemble dead limbs on the trees."

We came into the area of the nests and found it to be an extensive colony. The nests were as large as bushel baskets, sometimes four or five in a single tree. At first the village looked deserted.

"Study each tree closely," I whispered to Sonya. "There are lots of birds here, but you'll have to learn how to see them."

"I *do* see one," said the excited child, "standing right in that nest. How still he is! But I see the wind ruffling his feathers."

"And there are two almost directly above our heads." Giny pointed to the top of a basswood stub.

"I see three—four—five—six—oh, they're everywhere!" Sonya had her eyes trained now.

There were herons in every tree. The young of this year had attained full growth and were as large as the parent birds. I pointed out to Sonya several that were standing on one leg, balanced in the tops of trees.

"Do they know they look like dead branches?" she asked.

"They may not know what a dead branch is," I replied,

"but nature made them that way to hide even though they're right out in the open. Now let's count the nests."

We counted one hundred forty-seven nests. Sonya, who wanted this to be the largest colony ever found, insisted it was one hundred and fifty nests. At that it is likely we missed some.

"May I say that we found one hundred fifty?" she asked.

"Sonya, if you're going to be a naturalist you must be very accurate in your observations," I cautioned.

"One hundred and fifty!" Sonya said.

We ate in the rookery, using a moss-covered log as a bench and a large rock as a table. The herons concluded we meant them no harm and resumed activity. Young birds were trying their wings, old birds came and went, all keeping up a constant jabbering. They sailed overhead, eying us curiously.

Sonya loved her day in her *jungle,* and when we started for home the nest count was two hundred, according to her statistics.

"Shouldn't we say *about* two hundred, Sonya?" I asked. "We might have counted the same ones twice."

"Well, all right, *about* two hundred," she agreed reluctantly.

We returned to our island, and soon after dinner Dick came in his boat to get his daughter. He wore a worried look. It seemed to me that I caught a familiar scent about his clothing, but I said nothing.

"Where's Mother, Daddy?" asked Sonya.

"Yes, Dick," said Giny. "Why is it that you're alone? We expected Dorothy too."

"It's a sad story," Dick said, arching his eyebrows. "Dorothy is . . . indisposed!"

"Is she sick?" asked Sonya with immediate concern.

"No, dear." He patted Sonya's head. "She's not ill. I don't know just how to describe her condition. She's chagrined and maybe embarrassed, puzzled, irritated and decidedly unsocial."

"Don't be so mysterious," Giny put in. "What has happened?"

"I believe I scent the trouble," I said, glancing at Dick knowingly.

"Yes, I expect you do," he said. "Tell me—" he took on a pleading attitude—"what do you do to get rid of skunk odor?"

"Dick," cried Giny, "you don't mean that you got sprayed by a skunk!"

"No, I didn't, but Dorothy did!"

"Oh-h-h!" Sonya gasped.

"Poor Dorothy!" sympathized Giny. "How did it happen?"

Dick began the story with a shake of his head. "Well, after you left this morning we were pretty busy. We kept hearing some kind of a metallic noise outside in the brush and couldn't make out what it was. It was a sort of *click,* like hitting a can with a stick. It kept up so long we decided to investigate. We went outside and soon saw a skunk walking about with a can over his head. Apparently he had pushed his nose into the can to get some food and then couldn't get it out. It was over his nose and his eyes and he couldn't see where he was going, so he bumped into one tree after another."

"Oh, Daddy, didn't you take it off?" Sonya asked anxiously.

"Yes, we did," Dick answered sadly. "Dorothy said, 'Now what would Sam Campbell do if he were here?'

'Well, I suppose he would take that can off,' I replied.
And that's what he did. While she scratched his neck and
talked baby talk to him, I twisted and turned the can to
get it loose."

"You're a brave man," I interposed.

"Brave or foolhardy—I don't know which," Dick
moaned.

"Daddy, did you get it off?" Sonya was impatient.

"Yes. It came all at once. Maybe that was the trouble.
The skunk commenced to get nervous, and he beat the
ground with his feet and raised his tail. I gave one hard
jerk and the can came off, but I knocked him over. He
got to his feet thinking he was abused, and he turned loose
on the world in general. Oh, oh—what an ordeal!" Dick
held his hands to his head.

"And Dorothy got hit?" Giny asked.

"*Did* she?" Dick said. "That skunk's aim was perfect."

"Oh-h-h-h, poor Mother!" said Sonya.

"Poor Dorothy!" I said.

"I got just what the wind drifted to me," Dick went on,
"but Dorothy got the works. We burned the clothes she
had on. She has had five baths this afternoon, and she
plans to take several more tonight. What is there that
will take that odor out?"

"Once I got it out of a dog's collar by burying it for
three days," I replied.

Dick flashed a crooked smile at me. "Anything else?"
he asked.

"Yes, I've heard that you could wash it out with tomato juice, but I've never tried it."

"Come on, Sonya," said Dick resignedly. "We have a job to do."

"Are you going to bury Mother?" she asked in a little frightened tone.

"No, we're going to town for six cases of tomato juice!"

XXI

OVER THE MOONBEAM BRIDGE

IF DOROTHY ECK felt any resentment toward the animal kingdom because of her experience with the skunk, she concealed it. Two days later when we saw her she was still scrubbing and scouring. "If that is a skunk's idea of gratitude, I never want one of them to say 'thank you' to me again," she said. "And tomato juice? I'm through with it for life—I hope."

The main concern of both Dorothy and Dick was that the next two weeks be packed with nature experiences and camera opportunities for Sonya. "In two weeks we must leave for the city," Dick explained. "Sonya is to start school at that time."

"We must gather lots of memories and pictures for her," Giny agreed. "How about coming over this evening for more pictures of Loony Coon?"

"Fine! We'll be there," Dick said. "We have another adventure in mind too. Sonya's very fond of Warden Olie, you know."

"And he's fond of her," Giny put in.

"I'm sure he is. Now we wondered if you'd like to join us in a two-day stay at his place. We could rent two

186

of his cabins, have a chance really to visit with him and see more of his animals."

"We'd love it," Giny said enthusiastically. "I'll drop him a note today asking when the cabins are free. Of course, Warden Olie will have to talk it over with Grandmaw Honker."

"Please send word to Grandmaw that I shall dress my worst," Dorothy requested. "I hope she doesn't mind a little perfume—I seem to need it these days."

"That sounds grand," I said. "Two days with Warden Olie and Grandmaw will be wonderful. But about this evening—what do you say we try another campfire dinner? The moon is nearly full again, and there's no wind. We may not have many more days and nights like these."

"Splendid!" cried Sonya, jumping with delight. "Mother, could we take another angel-food cake?"

"Dare we?" Dorothy asked, looking at me.

"It seems an ill omen." I laughed. "But then, we don't believe in omens. Let's have a cake!"

"Goody!" Sonya shouted. Then she added with a little giggle that had much hope in it, "Maybe Loony Coon will get it again."

We gathered early at our campfire. Ada and Ray joined us. These two veteran nature lovers were always ready and anxious for any kind of outdoor activity.

Evenings are long in September. A chill permeates

the air the moment the sun goes down. We built the fire high and drew our table close to it for warmth.

"One really has to like picnics to do this," chattered Dorothy, as she put on an extra sweater.

"Anyway, there are no mosquitoes or flies," Dick observed.

"They have no ear muffs and gloves or they would be here," she replied. "By the way, what have we done with the cake? It's getting to be raccoon time."

"I just took it into the house and put it in the icebox," Giny said. "I locked all doors and put out other food for Loony Coon. If he gets it this time we might as well give up."

Sonya looked disappointed but didn't say anything.

"Look, folks, the show is on!" Ray pointed to the northeast shore of the lake. There the moon crept over the horizon, once again laying a sharply defined golden path right up to our island. We gazed at the spectacle for a long time.

"Mother, doesn't it look as if we could walk right up that golden bridge maybe into a wonderful land—maybe a wild world where everything is forest and animals?" Sonya was letting her fancy run free.

"And I think the animals are there all right," Ada broke in. "Listen!"

Far off in the direction of the rising moon we could hear the weird cries of a family of coyotes. Their voices started in low pitch, then rose in crescendo until they dominated the silence.

"Those are the first we've heard this year!" Giny exclaimed.

"And am I supposed to like that too?" Dorothy asked with a shudder.

"Yes," Giny insisted. "That cry is part of the wilderness."

"They won't hurt you, Mother," Sonya said consolingly. "They're like dogs."

Dorothy looked a question at me.

"Sonya's right," I said. "Coyotes do not attack people."

"Then maybe their call *is* sort of pretty," Dorothy conceded, looking in the direction of the howls. "But if they were merely inviting me to be their *pièce de résistance,* I couldn't see so much that's charming in it."

"They are predators, aren't they?" Dick asked.

"Yes," I replied. "The coyote is an important factor in the balance of nature. He lives on animals that are smaller than he—mice, wood rats, certain ground birds, rabbits. And, I suppose, raccoons when young might be among his victims."

"Speaking of raccoons," Ada said, "we have one with us now. Isn't that Big Boy?"

It was Big Boy, moving along in range of the firelight. There were several others with him, but none of them Loony Coon.

"Where's your pal, Big Boy?" Sonya asked, tossing him some bites of food. "You and Loony Coon are supposed to stay close together. Didn't you hear those coyotes?"

"Oh, oh—forgot something!" Giny exclaimed. "The cream—I'll go for it."

"Please let me," said the willing Sonya, rising. "I know where it is."

She took a flashlight and went running down the trail to the cabin. Dorothy looked after her adoringly. "I'm so grateful she hasn't the slightest fear of the woods or of darkness," she said. "When I was her age I wouldn't have done that for anything. What a foolish thing fear is!"

We heard the cabin door open and shut as the child went in. A moment later it opened again, but we didn't hear it close, nor did Sonya come skipping down the trail. Looking toward the cabin, I could see a flashlight playing about the woods. Then suddenly we heard her give a little scream and she called, "Mother, Daddy, come quick. Loony Coon is hurt!"

We left our table and hurried to the cabin. Sonya was in tears. "He came right up there." She indicated a clump of little balsam trees with her light. "And he has a fishhook fastened in his mouth. Then he ran away. What will we do?"

"Which way did he go?" I asked, searching about the brush with my light.

The raccoon answered the question by emerging from under a balsam tree. It was Loony Coon, floppy ear and all. Our lights were turned on him. Fastened firmly in one side of his lower jaw hung one of those vicious plugs used by fishermen. It had three gangs of hooks, one imbedded deeply in his flesh, the others dragging along on the ground. The pain he was suffering and the danger he was in were only too obvious.

We all tried to be calm and to find some solution for the distressing problem. We realized that we should not frighten Loony Coon or he might run through the woods and catch the dangling hooks on trees or even become entangled in them himself. The situation apparently had made him lose his confidence in us, for he would not come close.

"We must get a net and a pair of wire cutters." Ray spoke calmly out of his years of experience with animals and the woods. "We'll have to catch him and hold him still until we cut that hook."

I got the articles needed. Then we tried to approach Loony. He was wary of us and ran back into the brush.

"Loony Coon," cried Sonya, "don't you understand? We want to help you. Please come near."

I glanced up at Dorothy. There were tears in her eyes. "Loony Coon, we love you. Can't you trust us?" she added to Sonya's plea.

It was apparent that the young coon was hungry. Likely he had not eaten for many hours—as long as the hooks had been attached to him. We placed food out for him and he was able to get a few bites down, though with diffculty. But whenever we moved to approach him he ran away. We were feeling desperate.

"There must be a way to meet this," Giny said, her faith always rising when most needed. "There's the right thing to do and we have the intelligence to do it. Let's not be discouraged."

The fear haunted us that Loony Coon would grow so frightened he would leave. After we had made several attempts to catch him he was so suspicious he would not return to his food but merely peeked out at us from the brush.

"Marshmallows!" Giny exclaimed. "That's it—his favorite food. I'll get some."

Loony Coon responded to the marshmallows a little better, though this gave us no immediate solution. He would not come from the brush but picked up bites when we tossed them to him. One such bite lodged on a branch of a small cedar tree. Timidly Loony Coon reached for it. As he did the dangling hooks caught on another limb and held his head firmly. I suppose three men never moved faster than we did. Dick darted forward with the net and spread it over the struggling animal. I knelt beside him and endeavored to keep him from moving in a way that would increase his hurt. Ray reached for the hook with his wire cutters.

In spite of the advantage that had come to us, our task was not easy. The strength of the animal was amazing. Our combined strength seemed hardly equal to his, and had it not been that the hook held on the tree limb, he would have escaped from our grasp. Now desperate and not understanding our motives, he bit at us and clawed with his powerful front paws. Unavoidably we hurt him cruelly and he charged it against us. It seemed to him that his friends had suddenly become his enemies, and with his stout heart he fought fiercely. Each of us was to bear scars of that brief desperate struggle.

"Loony Coon," Giny called to him over our shoulders, "Loony Coon, we're only trying to help you. Can't you understand, little fellow? Please be patient." She continued to plead with him. The sound of her voice reassured him and momentarily he ceased his frantic fighting. That gave Ray the chance to reach in and cut in two the hook that was holding him. Quickly Ray grasped the other end and pulled it from his mouth. I picked up the plug and tossed it to one side so it would not catch in his flesh again.

Then we released the tortured creature. Despite our pleas, he raced off on the shortest route to the lake. His whole desire was to get away from this spot which seemingly had betrayed him. Out into the lake he swam, right down the moon's golden pathway. We called to him repeatedly but he sped on. He made a diminishing dot on the moon trail, getting smaller and smaller as he headed determinedly for the distant shore.

"Right into the land where the coyotes are," Dorothy said regretfully.

"He's a big coon now. I think he can take care of himself," I said, but my words did not sound very convincing.

Slowly and with drooping spirits we made our way back to the campfire, where we had left our dinner.

"Everything will be cold now," Giny said.

But it wasn't cold! In fact, the dinner wasn't—period! On the table were half a dozen coons, just cleaning up the last of everything. Big Boy was sitting in the butter dish, licking his paws. Blondy stood with two feet in a vegetable dish and the other in a bowl of gravy while he finished the strawberry preserves. Andrea had just about consumed a bowl of fruit salad. Glasses of milk had been tipped over, rolls knocked on the ground, olives and celery rolled all over the place, salad dressing and sugar were spilled together, and cottage cheese was mixed with everything.

"Oh," gasped Dorothy, "I don't know whether to laugh or to cry!"

"How would anyone like a nice peanut-butter sandwich for dinner?" asked Giny, her sense of humor returning somewhat. "I have some at the house."

"*Vive le* peanut butter!" I cried. "And we do have an angel-food cake."

The mention of it silenced the group again. We all looked out in the direction Loony Coon had gone.

"I don't believe I could eat any cake," Sonya said with a little sniffle.

"It doesn't seem so attractive as I thought it would be," Giny added.

"I'll take peanut butter," Dick said.

"I'd risk another run-in with a skunk if I could drop that cake right by Loony Coon's nose," Dorothy declared.

We watched until the moon rose higher in the sky and the golden trail was no longer.

"The moon took up its bridge," Sonya said sadly. "How will Loony Coon ever get back to us now?"

XXII

GRANDMAW IN THE DOGHOUSE

LOONY COON was constantly in our thoughts after the sad episode of the fishhook. Would he come back—or had the painful experience destroyed his confidence in us and sent him in search of new and perhaps gentler lands?

The next evening we watched anxiously for his appearance at the feeding station. Hours went by and he did not come. "Suppose we go over to the Eck cabin," Giny suggested. "Perhaps he's there."

We found Dorothy, Sonya and Dick keeping a constant watch, but Loony Coon had not been seen. Big Boy was there together with several others, all working energetically at the liberal repast placed out for him. Sonya pleaded with Big Boy. "You find Loony Coon, Big Boy. Please tell him we didn't mean to hurt him, won't you? Tell him to come back—we miss him."

Big Boy kept right on eating, never missing a single chew.

Giny and I decided to return to our island to see if our pet was there. Sonya's anxiety increased and her face wore a worried look that was out of place in her normally happy disposition. "If he *is* there, would you come right back and tell us?" she asked.

"I surely will, Sonya," I assured her.

"Even if it's in the middle of the night, will you come?" We promised. But there was no good news to report.

Through Ray and his forestry men we inquired about the country during the several days that followed. Word came that a friendly raccoon with an injured jaw had come to a lumberjack's cabin two miles to the east of us. We drove to the place, but the man who lived there said he saw the animal only once.

A day later a raccoon of similar description came to another backwoods cabin, a mile farther away than the first one. The report said it came to the door and knew how to open it. A trapper who lived there gave the coon some food but saw the animal no more.

We kept the Ecks informed of these happenings. "If that's Loony Coon, he's outward bound," I said regretfully. "It looks as if we have lost him."

Sonya ran into her room and closed the door to hide her tears.

"I won't give him up," Giny declared firmly. "Loony Coon is too important to us all. He *must* come back again."

"Yes, he *must!*" echoed Dorothy, looking in the direction of Sonya's room.

The time came for our two-day trip to Warden Olie's. By arrangement we stopped at the Eck cabin early in the morning to take them in our car. They came out to us, overnight bags in hand.

"You know, we nearly had to cancel this trip," Dorothy

declared as we placed the luggage in the trunk compartment. "Sonya didn't want to go."

"Sonya didn't want to go to Warden Olie's?" asked Giny in surprise.

"No."

"Well," Sonya said, feeling an explanation was due from her, "what if Loony Coon comes while we're gone? Who'd make him welcome?"

"Oh, we've left welcomes for him all over the place," Dick declared. "I've left enough food to feed all the coons in the country."

"Yes, Sonya," I added, "and we've left a great quantity out too. If Loony Coon comes back at all, you may be sure he'll stay. After all, we'll be gone only one night."

Sonya wasn't easily reconciled. She checked the food again and added a few cookies and marshmallows. Then we got in the car and began our journey.

"Did you shut the door?" Dorothy asked Dick.

"Yes, but I didn't lock it," he replied.

"No one ever locks doors in this country," Giny commented. "We never even think to do so."

"It simply amazes me," Dorothy added. "I must get over that habit before we go back to the city."

The beauty of the day and the excitement of the trip gripped our thoughts, so that Loony Coon was partially forgotten. We came to areas where the trees were in full autumn regalia. The red of maples, the orange of aspens and the yellow of birches blended in a sunburst of splendor. The sky was a deep azure, dotted with small, fluffy

clouds. Wayside streams and lakes reflected this loveliness.

Sonya started singing one of our favorite campfire
songs and we all joined in. We literally sang our way
through the journey.

Warden Olie was waiting for us when we arrived. He
walked out to our car, waving his arms in welcome. We
were much flattered by the way he had dressed for us.
His hair was combed and he wore a new shirt and new
trousers. In fact, he even had a tie on, though we didn't
see it until he pulled aside his whiskers.

"Look at that!" he said proudly. It was something to
see, though a little hard on the eyes with its yellow and
red stripes. "I ain't had one of them things on since the
last lumberjack ball. It's the only one I have—someone
left it in a cabin 'bout a year ago. Little flashy, eh?" He
replaced his whiskers.

After we had exchanged greetings Olie led us to our
two cabins. "I'm not much fer dollin' up," he said as we
took our bags in, "but I had to put on the dog for Sonya.
Cleaned the places up special fer ye, too. Bet ye can't
go-'head an' find a speck of dirt anywhere."

The two cabins he had prepared for us were immac-
ulate. They were rustic, almost crude, but comfortable
and woodslike. Most of the furniture he had made himself, and was right proud of his work.

"Where's Grandmaw Honker?" Sonya asked as we
came out of our cabins to look around.

"Grandmaw's in the doghouse!" Olie blurted out with

a nod of his head. She was, figuratively and literally.
Olie directed our attention to a place near the lake. "See
that doghouse?" he asked.

It wasn't hard to see, being unusually large and of the
same design as our cabins.

"Well, Grandmaw's in there," he went on. "The ornery
old critter. I'd like to go-'head an' pull her feathers out
and stuff 'em in a pillow."

"What has she done?" Dorothy asked.

"Done? Why she jist 'bout wrecked this place. We
used to have some peace around here, but not any more.
There, she's lookin' out now. See her?"

Grandmaw's long neck came poking out the ventilator
window. We all called our greetings and she gave a flat
squawk in reply.

"Yeh, ye know ye got company, don't you?" Olie grumbled. "Suppose you think I'll fergit everything and let
you out now. After the way you been actin' I ought to
keep you in there fer life. Oh, oh, there's Drummer.
That's why Grandmaw's gettin' so excited."

"Who is Drummer?" asked Sonya, staring toward
Grandmaw's doghouse.

"Drummer? Drummer's a grouse. Used to call 'em
pattridge, but now we find out they're grouse. He's hard
to see. Looks like the ground, but you can make him out
jist comin' up toward Grandmaw."

We could see the grouse walking in the slow timid way
characteristic of his kind. Grandmaw bent her serpent-
like neck toward him and jabbered a greeting.

"Tell us about Drummer," Dick said. "Where did he come from and what has Grandmaw Honker to do with him?"

"Plenty!" Olie ejaculated. "That's where all the trouble started. Look at 'em, thick as two doves. I found Drummer 'long the roadside a few days ago. Guess a car had hit him, for one wing was hurt. I looked him over. Wing wasn't broken, and I knew he'd be all right if nothin' caught him too soon. So I go-'head an' brought him home. He's a friendly fellow, and I kept him in my cabin fer a while. Then one day I put him out in the yard so he could eat some grass. Grandmaw was there, and someway she got the idea she was to be personal body-guard for that grouse. She walked round him jist looking him over and jabberin' all the time. Seemed to know he was hurt. She spread her wings and gave a honk that told the whole north woods to let that grouse alone. I tried to pick him up and take him back in the cabin, and she gave me a good thrashin'. Never saw her do it before.

"From then on she stuck closer to Drummer than the Secret Service does to our President. The worst of it is, she chases everything else off the place. My poor otters! She bit and tormented them until they left—been gone two days. My cat always liked to sleep on the back steps, but she made life so miserable for him I had to take him inside. She won't even let a squirrel or a rabbit or a chipmunk come in the yard while Drummer's there. I had to lock her up or I wouldn't have an animal left. And Drummer? He loves it!"

Olie pulled at his whiskers for a minute. "Course, it's
kinda cute." He chuckled. "After all, a wounded grouse
wouldn't last very long unless someone took care of it.
I'll go and let the ornery old critter out. You wait here;
she'll come to you."

When Olie opened the door of the doghouse Grandmaw emerged in queenly dignity. We heard Warden
Olie talking to her, giving all sorts of advice about her
future behavior, futilely. Drummer joined the big goose,
and they began making their way slowly toward us,
Drummer feeding on small seeds in the grass, Grandmaw
watching belligerently in various directions for any living
thing that dared approach. Warden Olie followed at a
safe distance.

"Sonya, get that picture!" Dorothy urged. "Isn't that
cute? That huge goose and that little grouse—what a
pair!"

A chipmunk went skipping across the ground, not
meaning any harm to anyone. Grandmaw took out after
the little creature, wings flapping, head pointed out like
a spear. With a series of squeaks the chipmunk vanished
into a hole in the ground. Old Black Joe, Olie's pet
raven, came coasting in and landed a few feet from Drummer. Grandmaw staged a bayonet charge that sent him
soaring into the sky again.

"See what I mean?" asked Olie, who had joined us.
"Nothin' is safe round here any more. Go-'head-in-there,
I don't know what to do. Either Drummer gets well and
leaves or I make a kettle of soup out of Grandmaw. Even

my chickadees ain't welcome. Oh, oh—" he pointed across the yard—"look what's comin'!"

Waddling along as if they had no place to go and all eternity in which to get there came two porcupines. We could hear their little call of "honk, honk," and it reminded Giny and me of our experience with our own porky pets Inky, and Salt and Pepper.

"Cute!" Giny exclaimed. "Why, Olie, you didn't tell us you had a pair of porcupines."

"Jist had 'em a week," Olie said. "Folks livin' a spell away had 'em at their summer cabin. They went home an' turned the porkies over to me."

"Are they friendly?" Dick asked.

"Ye never saw better go-'head-in-there pets in yer life," Olie replied. "Names are Jibber and Jabber. Now watch this."

He went to meet the two porkies, who were quite close by now. Stooping down, he grasped one in each hand, taking hold of the creatures by a front leg. He lifted them to his shoulder. Jibber and Jabber, obviously happy, talked and talked, playing about Olie's whiskers with their front feet.

"See?" he said. "Talk about bein' friendly—ye jist can't beat 'em."

For a few minutes Jibber and Jabber monopolized our attention. Olie demonstrated the correct way to handle them, and each of us—even Dorothy—took them up.

Dorothy was particularly thrilled at the novelty of this experience. She asked Sonya to snap a picture of her holding Jabber. "Think of it, I, Dorothy Eck, holding a real live porcupine and not shivering—that is, very much! I must have a picture or my friends will never believe I did it, and maybe a month from now I wouldn't believe it either."

Grandmaw Honker had no more tolerance of porcupines near her precious Drummer than any other animal.

When they were on the ground once more she rounded them up and pestered them until they climbed a tree. She had respect for their quills and didn't attempt to bite them. But she kept flapping her wings and raising such a fuss they finally climbed aloft to be rid of her.

Grandmaw came close to us after this. She was friendly, though Olie warned us not to get near Drummer. We noticed that the goose constantly kept between our group and the grouse.

"Look what I brought you, Grandmaw!" called Sonya, bringing out a shiny bracelet from her pocket. "See?" It's too small for me, and you can have it for your very own."

"Strange how that bracelet suddenly got too small for her," Dorothy whispered to me. "It was all right until she found out Grandmaw likes jewelry."

Grandmaw inspected the gift, gave several little squawks of admiration and then took it from Sonya. Forgetting Drummer for a moment, she went a few feet away and placed the bracelet under a bush.

"Now watch her go-'head an' get back here," said Olie, an impish twinkle in his eye. "Here, Drummer! Come on, Drummer!" He began walking right up to the grouse.

Grandmaw looked around in wild surprise at her own neglect of duty. Uttering challenging cries and beating the ground with her wings, she came hopping and running to the attack. Warden Olie swiftly got out of the way. "I don't want to tangle with the old critter when she's in a mood like that," he said. "She isn't foolin' one bit."

"And you're her best friend." Dorothy was critical of the goose. "Has she forgotten all you did for her?"

"Nope, nope." Olie was quick to defend her. "She's got a job to do and she aims to do it. Anyway, nothin's goin' to touch that grouse, and I guess I might as well go-'head an' admit I can't do anythin' 'bout the whole mess."

Grandmaw and Drummer slowly moved away, and we watched them and laughed at their antics. They disappeared into the woods, though we could trace their presence by the goose's constant jabbering.

Our day was filled with interesting experiences with the many friendly creatures that lived about Warden Olie's forest. While Grandmaw and Drummer were away, squirrels and chipmunks came to us. Old Black Joe came back. The big raven took food from us in most friendly fashion. Then he stopped, fascinated by something he saw on the ground. Suddenly he made a dash for the bracelet Grandmaw had left under a bush. Warden Olie moved quickly and reached the spot before Joe did.

"If Joe got that you'd never see it again," Olie said, putting the bracelet into his pocket. "Go on, you ol' black scamp! This belongs to Grandmaw."

"Oh, I should have brought him one too!" Sonya cried.

"Naw, you needn't," Olie said. "Joe would jist as soon have a piece of pop bottle. I'll give him something—but he can't have Grandmaw's bracelet."

Later Olie called in Jim the muskellunge, and Sonya caught a picture as the big fish broke water beside the pier.

The evening was a constant unfolding of adventures. The two otters Mike and Ike returned, much to Olie's delight. They came up through the trap door in the floor while we sat talking with the old woodsman. The animals were still dripping-wet from the lake, but they were nonetheless welcome. Olie coaxed them up into his lap. They soaked his new shirt and stained his one and only tie. "Go-'head-in-there!" Warden Olie exclaimed as he patted them. "I don't care what you do I'm so glad to see you. Didn't think you'd let that ol' Grandmaw drive ye completely out of the country. Looks like you're 'bout as glad to see me as I am to see you."

Mike and Ike were. They raced about the cabin nosing into every corner, then ran in their funny loping way back to Olie and climbed into his lap. Sonya made what was to be one of her most valued pictures when she caught the two of them engulfed in Olie's arms. One of them gave Olie's whiskers a playful but sharp tug. "Here, ye varmint—" he spanked the otter—"you know that makes me mad, don't you? I'll be makin' myself a winter coat out of your hide if you do that again."

The otter didn't seem much worried. A moment later he tugged at the whiskers again harder than before, and he kept his hide.

Now to the back door came Gray Boy, a friendly coyote, to receive food from Olie. Then came a beautiful gray fox, followed by three flying squirrels.

At midevening Warden Olie invited us to take a walk with him. He led the way silently down a forest trail until we came to a small clearing. Here he bade us wait and watch. There was a large cake of salt standing on an old stump. After a half hour of waiting we saw a beautiful ten-point buck emerge from the forest shadows and come to the salt lick. Olie whispered to us to stand still. "I raised him," he said, "and he won't let anyone else come near him. I call him King. Watch!"

Reflecting clearly the joy he was feeling, the old woodsman walked slowly toward the deer. At first the antlered head went up and the white tail lashed back and forth as if the buck were about to run. But at the sound of Olie's voice the animal calmed and resumed licking the salt. Olie advanced until he stood beside the graceful creature and then gently put his arm about its neck. It was an impressive scene.

"Isn't that beautiful?" Dorothy whispered. "As if we were looking into another world."

"Or rather getting a clearer view of this one," I added.

Warden Olie lingered long with King. At last the buck walked away, head erect, the very picture of regal dignity. Sonya ventured a flashlight picture, and the animal was not the least bit frightened.

Back at the cabin we stepped in to see Mike and Ike once more before retiring. They were asleep, huddled together on Warden Olie's bed. "Now look at that!" he grumbled. "I suppose I can sleep on the floor."

"Warden Olie," said Sonya, walking up to him.

"Yes, child." He put his arm about her.

"Would you tell a story before we go to bed? Something about the woods long, long ago?"

"Remember you promised us a story on our last visit," urged Dorothy.

Warden Olie looked down at Sonya, a big smile back of his whiskers. "Long, long ago," he mused as if the phrase had awakened a host of memories. He sat down in a chair and drew Sonya to his lap. We all sat down and gave him our attention. But he looked only at Sonya. "Yes," he said in a mood that was built for Sonya, "I'll tell you a story. It's a story for the likes of you. You other folks kin listen in ef ye want to, jist as long as you don't interrupt."

"We'll be good—if you only let us stay," Dorothy promised.

Warden Olie looked at Sonya for a moment. "Plegged ef I don't like ye jist 'bout as well as my otters," he said. "Always dreamed 'bout this—a young'un sittin' on my knee while I tol' yarns. Now ye see, Sonya, dreams can come true."

Sonya smiled and waited for the story.

XXIII

WARDEN OLIE'S YARN

"Long, long ago," the old woodsman began, smoothing his whiskers, "there was a big go-'head forest up in this north country better 'n any woods ye ever saw. Trees was bigger, lakes deeper, rivers faster, flowers prettier, skies bluer—and warn't nothin' livin' in it but animals, not a single human bein'. Animals got along right well together. They had some little problems, course, jist like we folks do. So they decided to organize sort of a government and rig up some laws to live by."

"But how do you know they did, Warden Olie?" Sonya interrupted. "If there was no person there to see the forest, who told you?"

"Well, ahem . . . Olie coughed and tugged at his whiskers. "Ye see, the woods still talks 'bout them days. If ye understand sech things, ye kin hear it in the cricket's song and when the wind whispers soft in the pine trees."

Sonya was satisfied and Olie went on.

"Coyote brought the animals together. He howled and howled till he rounded everybody up. They decided to pick out a boss first of all. Black Bear stood on his hind legs and waved his great paws for attention. 'I am the strongest one of all,' he said. 'I know the woods and am very wise. Who could be a better boss for ye than I?'

"Right then a voice came outa the air above, cryin', 'Chickadeedee! Chickadeedee! Chickadeedee!' Black Bear looked up at the mite of a bird and roared, 'Chickadee? Why, ye little feathered varmint, ye got a lot of nerve. Ye ain't strong 'nough to crush a hot snowflake!'

"Everybody laughed, but Chickadee perched on a limb. He ruffled up his feathers, tryin' to look as big as possible, and he kept shoutin' his name loud as he could. Black Bear waved his paws again and roared, 'How many want me fer a boss?' Everybody did, for Black Bear was mighty powerful. 'And who wants that little wart fer a boss?' he asked, laughin' and pointin' to the bird. And not one animal voted for him!"

"Oh," Sonya broke in sympathetically.

"Well, it didn't hurt him a bit! Next they had to go-'head an' choose their Second Boss. Gray Wolf let out a howl and said, 'I too am strong, wise and cunnin'—who would be better Second Boss than I?' And right away from the tree came 'Chickadeedee! Chickadeedee! Chickadeedee!' 'Why, you undersized flying ant,' Gray Wolf said, 'you couldn't handle an angleworm! How many want me for Second Boss?' Everyone did, and Chickadee didn't get a single vote. They just laughed at him."

"Couldn't Chickadee be Third Boss?" asked Sonya, entering wholeheartedly into the story.

"Naw," said Olie. "Wild Cat was Third Boss and

Coyote was Fourth Boss. In fact, Chickadee was jist a big joke as far as they were concerned, and they finally made him forty-second assistant office boy. It didn't offend him, though. He go-'head an' flew away shoutin' his name, 'Chickadee, Chickadee,' proud as could be.''

Warden Olie paused for a moment, smoothed his whiskers, flashed a wink at Dick and then continued.

"Well, things went along pretty good for a long while in that forest long, long ago. Most of 'em obeyed their laws, and it was right go-'head-in-there peaceful. Then one day Barred Owl came flyin' in much excited. He had seen a new animal, and his eyes got big as saucers and red as a toadstool. 'It's a tall thing,' he told Boss Black Bear, 'stands on its hind legs and uses its front legs as a raccoon does. Never saw one like it before.' 'Sounds new to me,' said Black Bear. 'Mebbe Raven knows what it is—he seems to know everything.' Raven did know and his feathers shivered when he said, 'I'm afraid it's White Man.' 'Y're afraid?' roared Black Bear. 'Afraid, with me around? Am I First Boss here, or am I? You keep watch on this . . . what did you call him?' 'White Man,' said Raven. 'Yeah, White Man.' Black Bear had a little sneer on his face an' then he said, 'Raven, if he does anything wrong, you tell me.' 'I'll watch him,' said Raven with another shiver, 'but I'm plumb scared.'

"Well, Raven watched White Man every day, and what he told the animals didn't make anyone happy. White Man cut trees and built himself a cabin. Then he cut more trees and more trees. Some trees were the homes of

squirrels, others the homes of birds. He built a big fire
of brush and the flames spread, burnin' up lots of trees
before the rain came and put the fire out.

"One day Coyote came in runnin' on three feet and
holdin' up one paw that had been hurt. 'White Man go-
'head an' puts his teeth out on the ground,' he screamed,
groanin' with pain. 'He has teeth all up an' down the
river. One of 'em bit me and I had a hard time gettin'
away.' 'Those aren't his teeth,' said Raven. 'Those are
traps. I've seen 'em before, and they're awful!'

"Now Black Bear was plumb mad. He roared and
grunted around. 'It's 'bout time he finds out who's First
Boss of these woods,' he said, rising on his hind legs.
'Raven, go tell that what-you-call-it to come over here.
Tell him I, Black Bear, First Boss of these woods, want
to see him.' 'I'll go, but I'm scared,' said Raven, and he
was off. In a few minutes a loud *bang* sounded through
the woods, and Raven came flyin' back like wild. His
tail feathers were all gone. 'He shot at me,' he screamed,
so frightened his feathers turned part white. 'He has a
gun. I saw guns before and they hit awful hard. Oh, my
poor tail feathers!' "

"Oh," came another exclamation of sympathy from
Sonya.

"Black Bear was really mad now," Ollie went on,
thoroughly caught up in his own story. "He called all the
animals together to decide what to do. 'I've had enough
of that go-'head-in-there White Man, whatever he is,' he
roared. 'We'll drive him from the woods. We'll tear him

limb from limb.' Black Bear got himself all worked up. He waved his great paws to show his strength. He hit the trees with his claws an' made splinters fly. He bit into stumps an' tore out great chunks of wood with his teeth.

"Standin' up to his full height, he beat his chest an' said, 'Of all of us, who is the best to run this new meddlin' animal out of the forest? Who is, I ask ye?' And then from overhead came a voice sayin', 'Chickadeedee! Chickadeedee!'

"Black Bear was flabbergasted. He looked up at the Chickadee as if he'd like to swallow him with one gulp. 'Why, you little feather-coated hunk of nothin',' he screamed, 'you couldn't fight a mosquito with its bill cut off. I'm the one to handle this White Man. I don't know where he came from, but I'm drivin' him back there.' And away he went through the woods headed for the place where White Man lived.

"He was jist barely out of sight when another bang echoed through the woods. There was a wild scramble, and here came Black Bear back a lot faster 'n he went, breakin' down brush and gruntin' his loudest. 'Wow!' he roared. 'Out of my way! He used that gun on me and half of my left ear is gone. I can't go-'head an' fight anythin' like that! Anyone else want to go after him?' And for the first time in his life Black Bear looked scared. Then came a little voice out of a tree callin', 'Chickadeedee, Chickadeedee!'

"Don't bother us at a time like this, you cipher with the

circle gone,' Black Bear yelled. 'Gray Wolf, you're cunnin' and strong—s'pose you drive that fellow out.' "

"And did he do it—did he chase White Man out?"
Sonya asked.

"He did *not!* He came howlin' back with the end of
his tail shot off! Then Wild Cat cried out, 'I have sharp
fangs and claws, I fight fiercely. Who could do this better than I?' 'Chickadeedee, Chickadeedee,' came the
voice from the tree. 'Miaow!' screamed Wild Cat, even
wilder than usual. 'Go play with a butterfly. Y're not an
animal, y're jist a pest. Let me at White Man.' And off
through the woods he went.

"There was another big bang from over near White
Man's home, but Wild Cat didn't come runnin' back as
the others did. The other animals waited and waited, but
no Wild Cat. Then Raven flew over to see what had happened. He looked right funny without his tail feathers,
but he could fly jist the same. In a few minutes he came
back double-time. 'Oh, I saw Wild Cat,' he screamed.
'He's nailed to the cabin door, jist his hide. He's never
comin' back!'

"The animals were pretty much discouraged now.
Their best bosses couldn't fight White Man, and what
could the rest of 'em do? Black Bear sat nursin' his ear,
Gray Wolf lickin' the end of his tail, and Coyote held up
his paw.

" 'Would anyone else like to go after White Man?'
grunted Black Bear. 'Or must we admit that we're
beaten?'

" 'Chickadeedee, Chickadeedee,' came from the air, and the bird flew around and around Black Bear's head. 'Not you, you varmint,' he roared, 'not you . . .' And then he stopped. 'Wait a minute!' he said. 'Maybe that's a good idea. Yes, ye can go! That's one sure way to get rid of ye.'

" 'Chickadeedee, Chickadeedee, Chickadeedee,' the bird cried at the top of his voice, and he flew off toward White Man."

"Warden Olie," Dorothy broke in, 'if you're going to have Chickadee shot by White Man, I'm going to leave right now."

"Now don't get in a hurry," said Olie with a twinkle in his eyes. "Jist stick around and see how this comes out. Kin I help what happens in the story?"

"Go on, Mr. Olie, please," Sonya said anxiously.

"Well, White Man went a-choppin' trees. He got a mite hungry afterwhile and sat on a stump while he ate some sourdough bread and cheese. He was plumb surprised when somethin' went whizzin' past his ear, callin', 'Chickadeedee, Chickadeedee!' 'What in tarnation is that?' he said. The bird lit on a tree limb 'bout ten feet away and jist kept callin', mixin' in a little 'Phoebe, Phoebe' for variety. 'So y're a Chickadee,' White Man said. 'I wouldn't boast about it ef I was you—ye don't amount to much.'

"But Chickadee jist called his name all the louder and fluffed up his feathers. Some crumbs of sourdough fell from White Man's hand, and Chickadee went right to his feet and picked them up. 'Now look at that,' White Man said. 'Ye ain't afraid, are ye?' He put some more crumbs down. Chickadee got them too. White Man put some on his knee and the bird came after them. 'Bless ye!' said White Man. 'I wouldn't have believed it.' And he gave Chickadee more. When lunch was finished and White Man had to work more he tossed the rest of his food out for the bird. 'It's good havin' company, Chickadee,' he said. 'Guess I been lonesome and didn't know what was the matter. Will ye come agin?'

"After that Chickadee came again every day and had lunch with White Man. The other animals wondered what was goin' on, and they came and peered out of the woods to see. To their amazement there was Chickadee sittin' right on White Man's head.

" 'I see that bear again!' White Man said to Chickadee. 'Watch me take a shot at him.'

"But when White Man was aimin' his gun Chickadee hopped right up on the barrel, and White Man couldn't see to shoot. 'Okay, little one,' said White Man. 'Someway I don't hanker to pull the trigger nohow. Mebbe Black Bear is a good sort of fellow ef ye git to know him.' "

"I'm beginning to like White Man!" Sonya exclaimed.

"Well, he wasn't so bad," Olie agreed. "He and Chickadee got to be pals. They stayed together all day long. Then funny things started happenin'. White Man gathered in his traps. Said he didn't want to hurt animals.

He put his gun away and stopped shootin' them. Next he go-'head-in-there an' put food out fer them, and he helped them when they was hurt or sick.

"Then the animals held a meetin' again. Everybody was happy at what had happened to White Man. 'Chick-adee did it,' cried wise Old Owl. 'He beat White Man jist with love. And he showed us love is stronger 'n your paws, Black Bear; better 'n your fangs, Gray Wolf!'

"Raven spread his wings and shrieked for attention. His new tail was black and beautiful. 'And who is strongest among us, who ought to be First Boss?' he asked. "Chickadeedee, Chickadeedee,' called a little voice overhead, as the tiny bird came flyin' in.

" 'Yes,' cried Raven, 'Chickadee is our First Boss. What do you say?'

" 'Woosh a-dee-dee,' Black Bear grunted.

" 'Ah-oo-o-o-o a-dee-dee,' Gray Wolf howled.

" 'Arf-a-dee-dee,' barked the Fox.

"And such a mixture of howls, barks, whines, chatters, calls, grunts and whistles went up as was never heard before in the forest. So Chickadee was made First Boss of all the animals!"

"And did he boss White Man too?" Sonya asked.

"He shore did," Olie said with a quick nod of his head. "Bossed him like nobody's business. He bosses him even to this day. And so the animals and White Man learned to live together happily—all because they learned to love one another."

Olie's story was done. It may have been told for Sonya, but we all enjoyed it as much as did she. We rose to go to our cabins for the night.

"Warden Olie," said Sonya with a sleepy smile.

"Yes, child."

"It was a nice story. Thank you. But wasn't it just a little . . ." she hesitated.

"Now go-'head, little sweet one," Olie said. "What did ye want to ask?"

"Well, I like your story anyway, but wasn't it just a little bit true—some of it?"

Warden Olie laughed outright. "Bless you, child," he said. "I can't be sure about all that happened among the animals, but I know what happened to that go'head-in-there White Man—fer that was me!"

XXIV

TROUBLE RETURNS

THE next morning Grandmaw Honker had to be put in the doghouse early. She went on a rampage that was something to behold. We heard Warden Olie out on the lake shore at daybreak, trying to keep peace in his family. A dozen animal voices were talking all at once, each trying to tell his side of the story.

We stepped out of our cabins to see what was going on in this soft gray light of morning. Drummer was there, and right beside him was Grandmaw acting like a one-goose revolution. Jibber and Jabber were there, and we could distinguish their soft grunts in the melee. The two otters were on hand too; so were Big Foot the rabbit, Joe the raven and a number of others, all trying to get to the food Warden Olie had for them. But Grandmaw was making them all decidedly unwelcome.

"Ye long-necked nuisance!" we heard Olie say. "Let the otters alone, they won't hurt yer old grouse. Now don't tangle with them porcupines or you'll be mighty sorry. Here, stay away from Big Foot. Let Joe alone. That chipmunk won't hurt yer pattridge."

And so it went. Grandmaw nipped everyone. We heard one yipe after another as she undertook to enforce her decree that all of them had to disappear when Drummer was around. Presently they were gone, and only the big goose and little grouse strutted about.

"Now look at that! Go-'head-in-there look what ye went and done!" Olie remonstrated. "None of them folks had their breakfast and, ye old witch ye, ye chased them away. Ef ye think I'm goin' to stand fer that, ye got another guess a-comin'. Into the doghouse ye go, till these folks eat!"

"Squawk!" went Grandmaw, as Warden Olie wrapped his long arms about her and lifted her from the ground. She was an armload for him, though. One wing got free of his grasp and beat the air furiously. Then the other one got loose, but Olie held onto the rest of Grandmaw and waddled over to the doghouse. He poked the reluctant goose inside and shut the door. Immediately her head and long neck came out the window and she gave a series of resentful squawks.

"Yell all ye want to," Olie panted. "Learn how to behave yourself and ye won't get put in jail. Now stay there till these other folks get somethin' to eat."

Olie heard our laughter now and signaled us to come down to him. "Sorry my children misbehave," he apologized. "I do my best to train 'em right. Now, want to help me serve breakfast?"

We did. Presently we had as guests two porcupines, one fox, one cat, one raven, two crows, two otters, three chipmunks, one grouse and a squirrel. Grandmaw watched from the window in the doghouse, thinking what a disturbance she could cause if she were only free.

Sonya took some bites of bread to her and the goose accepted them, but her actions showed she would still like to get out there and start another riot.

It was not until we had eaten breakfast and the day was well under way that Grandmaw Honker was released. All the animals were gone except Jibber and Jabber, so she chased them up a tree and then took up her vigilant guard over Drummer.

"Watch this!" said Olie, pointing to the pair of birds. They were walking slowly toward the lake. "Grandmaw tries her best to make a goose out o' that pattridge."

They were struggling along, Grandmaw in the lead, Drummer following a few feet behind. The goose waddled right into the water and swam with the easy grace of her kind. The grouse walked to the edge of the lake and stopped. He looked at his bodyguard curiously and gave his short chirping call. Grandmaw said a few things to him in goose language that could probably have been interpreted as "Come on in, pal; the water's fine." But Drummer chirped back, "Sorry, slugger, but my people don't do such things. Better come out of that before you get all rusty."

Grandmaw decided leadership was needed, so she came out on shore again, marched the grouse in a circle and then led the way into the water. Drummer stopped short as before, and the argument went on between them. Then Grandmaw decided to use more forceful measures. She came out on shore, got back of Drummer and tried her best to push him into the water. Drummer wouldn't stand for this. He bent his head low to the ground and made a run for the nearest bushes. Grandmaw followed him, looking back resentfully at our laughter.

"Ye see," Olie called to her, "even you can't boss everybody."

Sonya and Dorothy decided to take a walk down one of the forest trails. Things were quiet for the time being

in Olie's menagerie. Jibber and Jabber were the only animals in sight, and they were high in a tree.

Sonya tapped on the tree and called to them, but they wouldn't come down. "I guess it's time for their morning nap," she said to Olie.

"It's always time fer their nap," he answered. "Porcupines are the sleepin'est things I ever saw. They just go from one nap to another. Mebbe when ye come back from your hike they'll be more sociable. Take that trail yonder." He pointed to a pathway leading away from his clearing. "It leads to a little lake where there's a beaver house. Beavers may not be there, but jist make yourselves at home."

Dorothy and Sonya had a many-sided adventure on this woodland walk. In later conversations we learned from them of their experiences. They had the feeling that they were wandering in Warden Olie's woods of "long, long ago." They had not gone far when a grouse flew up at their very feet with his noisy flurry of wings, frightening Dorothy nearly out of her shoes. She practically stepped on a rabbit, and the bewildered bunny went dashing through the underbrush. "The only reason I didn't climb a tree was because I couldn't move a muscle," Dorothy said in telling of the incident.

They reached the small lake and stood in silence looking out at the beaver house near the shore. Their silence and Dorothy's peace of mind were broken when there was a startling crash close to them in the woods. A large, decayed birch tree had given way and fallen to the ground. "I jumped straight up in the air and had a hard time to get down again," Dorothy recounted the experience. "I know at least a dozen bears must have pulled that tree down." Was Sonya frightened? Not in the least. She was having a wonderful time consoling her mother and assuring her that nothing would harm her.

Then a pine cone fell from a tree and struck Dorothy

on the head. It wasn't a hard blow, but it was wholly un-expected and brought forth one of Dorothy's pet shrieks. "Sonya," she exclaimed, "we must go back! This whole forest is against me. Next thing some monkeys will be pelting me with coconuts."

"Coconuts don't grow here, Mother, and neither do monkeys," Sonya said.

"Well, then, lions will throw bananas at us," her mother insisted, starting down the trail.

They had come in sight of the clearing about Warden Olie's cabins when they saw a waddling porcupine com-ing to them. "Look, Mother," cried Sonya. "It's Jibber, or else it's Jabber."

"So it is," Dorothy agreed. "And now, Sonya, dear, watch your mother. I know just how Warden Olie handles this fellow."

She walked unhesitatingly up to the slow old creature, talking to it constantly. Boldly taking it by the front feet, she lifted it up and brought it to rest on her arm. "See?" she asked Sonya. "Didn't I do that well? Come on, we'll take Jibber to Jabber, or Jabber to Jibber, as the case may be."

We saw Sonya and Dorothy come marching out of the woods, Dorothy holding the porcupine proudly for us to see.

"What ye got there?" Olie asked.

"Jibber or Jabber," Dorothy answered with a smug smile.

"Can't be," said Olie. "My two porkies is still up a tree. See 'em yonder?"

Sure enough, we could make out Jibber and Jabber still engrossed in their nap in the very tree they had climbed hours back.

Dorothy's eyes grew larger and larger as light dawned on her. Her mouth dropped open. "Then, wh-wh-what is this thing?" she whispered.

"Looks to me like ye picked up a wild porky," Olie said calmly. "No more tame ones about here."

"Ee-e-e-e-e-ek!" screamed Dorothy, hurriedly depositing the porcupine on the ground.

Up went the porky's quills, and he ran in his funny half-sideway manner for the woods, doubtless wondering what kind of animal he had found that picks a fellow up and carries him affectionately one minute and plunks him on the ground the next.

"Why, oh, why, does everything happen to me?" Dorothy asked when she could speak once more. We could see shivers run from her head to her feet, one after another.

"Guess nature is sort of initiating you into her clan," Olie suggested.

The remaining hours at Olie's were packed with interest. Grandmaw got out of the doghouse on her promise of good behavior. She remembered the bracelet Sonya had brought to her and went to the bush where she had left it. Warden Olie had the jewelry in his pocket, and he hurried over to drop it on the ground for the goose. She picked up the bright article and carried it about in her beak for some time, then hid it again.

We watched the goose as she went for a swim. Suddenly she took off on her wings and soared high above the treetops. "She's flyin' more lately," Warden Olie commented. "It's gittin' near time fer geese to go south, an' I guess she's trainin' up fer the trip. I'll miss the go-'head-in-there old nuisance."

Sonya was nearly in tears when she bade Warden Olie farewell. "Nope, little chickadee," he said, taking her in his arms. "Woods people don't cry. No tears now." And then he had to wipe some from his own eyes.

It was late in the evening when we reached the Eck cabin on our return from Olie's. "So much has happened I feel as if we've been away from here for a month," Dorothy said.

"It's given us wonderful memories to live on during the winter," Dick said.

Sonya said nothing. Woods people don't cry, and there were still tears trying to get out.

We walked over to the cabin door with the Ecks. "Every scrap of food I put out is gone!" Dick exclaimed. "We must have fed a mob of raccoons."

"The garbage can is tipped over," Dorothy noted.

Sonya reached in the screen door and turned on lights

in the cabin kitchen. "Mother!" she cried. "Mother, look!"

We were all beside her quickly. What a sight met our eyes! The house looked as if it had passed through a private earthquake. "Coons have been in the house!" Dick declared with a groan. "They opened the door and went in."

"Opened the door?" Sonya was excited. "Loony Coon could do that. Is he back?"

"My house! Look at it!" Dorothy was just realizing the extent of the mess before us. Canisters that had stood on the kitchen counter had been tipped over, and flour, sugar, tea and coffee were mixed in one grand conglomeration over floor and sink. Cans and condiments had been pulled off cabinet shelves. Boxes of breakfast food, packages of raisins, crackers, dry beans, corn meal and other ingredients had been combined in one wild mixture. Raccoon paw marks were all over the floor and up the wall.

"The icebox has been opened!" Dorothy cried as we made our way with difficulty through the debris. "Oh, look at this!" Eggs, oranges, butter, mustard, salad dressing, vegetables—all were in disorderly piles right where they had fallen, and had been mixed by raccoon feet.

"Oh, can we buy the cabin and just burn it down," Dorothy moaned, wringing her hands. "We can never clean this up."

"I have news for you," Dick said. He had just switched

on the light in their living room. "Your guest has been in here too."

"No! no!" begged Dorothy. "What did he do in there?" There was no need to answer. A look into the next room told all. The books were pulled out from the shelves and lying all over the floor. Floor lamps were overturned. Several potted plants lay upside down on the floor, the dirt and flowers spread far and wide. A bottle of ink was overturned on the desk, the black fluid lying in a puddle from which led the black tracks of raccoon feet. A box of chocolate candy had been discovered by the intruder and the contents were gone. Dorothy put her hands over her face to shut out the picture.

"Mother," Sonya said softly.

Mother didn't answer at first.

"Mother," came Sonya's voice again, "do you see what I see?"

Dorothy looked up and followed the direction of Sonya's pointing finger. All our eyes came to rest on a round puddle of flour, jam, jelly and what-not mixed with fur, curled up in the middle of Dick's favorite chair.

Even as we watched speechlessly, the puddle began to move. Paws and legs emerged. Then a besmirched raccoon with sleepy eyes and a droopy left ear sat up, stretched and yawned.

"*You!* You, villain!" I shouted, pointing my finger accusingly at the animal.

Up came the left front foot in that circular gesture that said, "Hi!"

"Loony Coon!" cried Sonya, running to him. "Loony Coon, it *is* you—you came back. Oh, Loony Coon!"

We all looked at Dorothy. Would this ordeal be too much for her? What would be the reaction to this horrible mess in her home?

She was staring at Sonya, now kneeling beside the young raccoon. "Isn't that the cutest thing you ever saw?" she asked.

And she joined Sonya on her knees, while they both stroked Loony Coon's flour-powdered head!

XXV

SWEET DREAMS

WINTER slowly tightened its grip on the north country. October was gone and the first frosty days of November were at hand. Flights of wild geese frequented the sky. Fifty-four of their wedge-shaped squadrons went by within sound range of our island in a single day. We heard them in the night too, talking persistently in their strange tongue as they headed southward.

Somewhere in this mass migration was Grandmaw Honker. A scribbled note came from Warden Olie saying she had disappeared into the air one dawn. "Didn't see her go," Olie wrote, "but I heard her squawking high over the cabin, jist after a big flight of geese went by. She's been so ornery I was hopen she would go, but now thet she's gone, dogged if I ain't counten the days till spring when she comes back again. Well, anyway, Mike and Ike will have some peace now. So will Jibber and Jabber. But, you know, they act sorta lonesome too."

We had our own problem of loneliness to handle. Sonya, Dorothy and Dick had left for the city where school and work awaited them. We promised we would keep food out at their cabin until the raccoons went into their winter sleep. Nothing can look emptier or lonelier than a woodland cabin boarded up for the winter. On our visits there we completed our errand as quickly as possible and hurried away from the place.

Sonya was happy at school, we heard. Almost daily she was called on to tell her little classmates something of her experiences in the north woods. The names of Loony Coon, Big Boy, Andrea, Grandmaw Honker, Pestersome Pete and the other animals were known throughout her school.

A letter came from Dorothy. "You will receive a package soon," it said. "This is Sonya's idea. You may eat what it contains yourself, or give it to Loony Coon as you wish. I predict he will get most of it. We had a wonderful summer. So many things happened, it seems to us that years went by. I have never known Dick to be so happy before. And Sonya? She simply entered a paradise and stayed there. And I? I wish you could see me. As I write this there is a cat asleep in my lap, a dog curled up against my feet and our new canary bird is perched on my shoulder. All this and only one shiver. How am I doing?"

The promised package arrived in due time, and it was an angel-food cake! The jolting in the mail had pushed it out of shape somewhat, but it was still fresh and delicious. We shared it with the raccoons, but not so generously as Sonya would have desired.

On Sonya's insistence we sent them a regular bulletin on the happenings in our forest world. There was plenty to tell. One item of news Giny sent by special delivery, knowing how it would please Sonya. "Loony Coon and

Andrea are pals once more," she wrote. "In fact, all babies and mothers are traveling and playing together again." The weaning period was over, and the young animals had learned to take their living from the forest. This accomplished, Andrea and Lady no longer snarled and snapped at their offspring. We saw Loony Coon and Andrea *wuzzling* once more, and they sometimes played just as they had in early summer months.

The first drowsy hours of their winter sleep were upon the coons. They moved about sluggishly and frequently took naps about the feeding area. On colder evenings they often gathered in little clusters in protected places, helping to keep one another warm.

Then came the days when it was difficult for us to go to and from our island. Ice formed across the lake, too thin to bear our weight and yet too thick to plow through with the boat. For several days we could chop our way through, but soon this was impossible and we had to live in town until the ice was thicker. Finally winter reigned supreme over the forest. No longer did we hear the voices of geese overhead, and the coons came no more to the feeding stations.

When we went to our island now it was on snowshoes. The first blizzard of winter coated the north country with a blanket of ermine. The ice had thickened to such an extent automobiles could be safely driven across the lakes.

Animal life was scarce in the forest. Deer retreated far back into the great swamps, there to yard and weather the winter. Bears were asleep. Once on a snowshoe hike we came upon a bear den made under the upturned roots of a fallen tree. A thick drift of snow had gathered here, but out of a little vent came a tiny curl of vapor caused by bruin's breathing. We knew it was best not to disturb him.

To our feeding station came an ermine, the name given the weasel when he has his pure-white coat of winter. He was a beautiful creature and fed energetically on bones and suet we put out for him. While this little animal has a reputation of being a vicious killer, we found no evidence of the trait in the one before us. Squirrels and birds came within easy reach of him, and he made no move toward them.

We found a number of places where raccoons were sleeping the winter away. Under a shed on our island six were huddled together, and one of them we identified as Big Boy. Several other groups were located under neighboring cabins on the mainland.

One day we chanced close to the hollow maple tree called Coony Castle. We slipped off our snowshoes and stepped up to the opening to look inside. There were three raccoons, fitted as snugly together as mosaic in a floor. *One of them had a left ear that dropped against his head and a streak of white fur between his ears!*

"It's Loony Coon!" Giny cried excitedly. "He's made his winter home in the very tree home where he was born. What news for Sonya!"

"And that's Andrea with him," I added. "Likely the third one is another member of the family."

"How sound asleep they are!" Giny said, studying them closely. "What do you suppose Loony Coon is dreaming right now?"

"Oh, about angel-food cakes and marshmallows," I suggested.

"And peanuts and watermelons!" Giny added.

"And screen doors to open and houses to ruin!"

"And new ways to worry Sonya, Dorothy, Dick, Giny and Sam," said Giny.

"And the time when the world is warm again, spring is in the air, the waters flow once more and he can search the shallow waters for crawfish and bloodsuckers. . . ."

"Ugh!" Giny shuddered. "I don't like them even in Loony's dream!"

Our toes tingled with the cold. It was time to move on. We took one more look at the somnolent raccoons.

"Sleep on, pets," Giny said. "Just don't dream about fishhooks and owls. When you feel spring shaking you by the shoulder, wash your faces and swim over to the island. We'll have breakfast ready and waiting for you."